CRCT

Workout

Mathematics

Grade 5

Triumph Learning®

A Haights Cross Communications ➤®Company

Jerome D. Kaplan, Ed.D.

Professor Emeritus

Seton Hall University

CRCT Workout, Mathematics, Grade 5
145GA
ISBN-10: 1-59823-910-4
ISBN-13: 978-1-59823-910-2

Author: Jerome D. Kaplan, Ed.D.
Cover Image: © Polka Dot Images/Jupiter Images

Triumph Learning® 136 Madison Avenue, 7th Floor, New York, NY 10016

Dear Student,

Are you a math champion?

You will be when you use

Workout!

Getting in shape is easy. Just complete the lessons inside.

So, on your mark, get set –

Work OUT!

Table of Contents

LESSON 1 Factors and Multiples

 **Review It!** When you work with factors and multiples, remember these words:

product the result of multiplication

factor when two whole numbers are multiplied, each is a factor of the product

2 and 4 are **factors** of 8.

multiple the product of a whole number and a counting number (1, 2, 3, 4, ...)

32 is a **multiple** of 8.

Find the first five multiples of 12 and all factors of 12.

Step 1   Multiply to find multiples.

$12 \times 1 = 12$
$12 \times 2 = 24$
$12 \times 3 = \underline{\hphantom{000}}$
$12 \times 4 = \underline{\hphantom{000}}$
$12 \times 5 = \underline{\hphantom{000}}$

◄┄┄┄┄┄┄┄┄┄┄┄┄ **REMEMBER** Multiply 12 by 1, by 2, by 3, ...

Step 2   Start with 1 to find factors.

$1 \times 12 = 12 \longrightarrow$ 1 and 12 are factors.

$2 \times 6 = 12 \longrightarrow$ 2 and 6 are factors.

$3 \times 4 = 12 \longrightarrow$ 3 and 4 are factors.

12 has _____ factors in all.

So, the first five multiples of 12 are _____ and the factors of 12 are _____ .

Find the first 6 multiples of each number.

 **Ask Yourself**

1. 5 _____   **2.** 9 _____

3. 11 _____   **4.** 8 _____

5. 16 _____   **6.** 15 _____

7. 25 _____   **8.** 100 _____

1.

What number do you multiply by first? 0, 1, or 2?

Find the factors of each number.

9. 10 _____   **10.** 13 _____

11. 15 _____   **12.** 18 _____

13. 24 _____   **14.** 60 _____

15. 21 _____   **16.** 36 _____

9.

Which is a factor of 10? 2, 3, or 4?

Solve.

17. Ellie works at a camp. Her age is a multiple of 6 and a multiple of 8. What is the youngest age Ellie could be?

_____

17.

Which is a multiple of 6? 3 or 12?

18. Felo is thinking of a number between 50 and 60. One of its factors is 9. What is Felo's number? _____

On Your Own!

Circle the best answer for each question.

1. Which is a multiple of 4?

    A. 2

    B. 10

    C. 14

    D. 20

2. Which is a factor of 80?

    A. 9

    B. 15

    C. 20

    D. 25

3. Which is NOT a factor of 16?

    A. 2

    B. 4

    C. 6

    D. 8

4. Which is NOT a multiple of 14?

    A. 32

    B. 56

    C. 70

    D. 98

5. Which list shows all of the factors of 20?

    A. 1, 2, 4, 5, 20

    B. 1, 2, 4, 5, 10, 20

    C. 1, 2, 4, 5, 6, 10, 20

    D. 1, 2, 4, 5, 6, 8, 10, 20

6. Jeff is thinking of a number less than 100. It is a multiple of 10 and a multiple of 20. What is the greatest number Jeff could be thinking of?

    A. 90

    B. 80

    C. 60

    D. 30

7. Ariana baked apple turnovers. She can divide the turnovers into equal groups of 3 or equal groups of 4. Which of these could be the number of turnovers Ariana baked?

    A. 7

    B. 16

    C. 30

    D. 36

8.   **Part A.**   Write the factors of 22.

_____

_____

           Part B.   Use the numbers from Part A to write a sentence that includes the word "multiple."

_____

_____

_____

 Fill in the blanks.

9.   Since 6 × 7 = 42, 42 is a _____ of 6.

10.   Since 6 × 7 = 42, 6 is a _____ of 42.

11.   When two numbers are multiplied, the result is called the _____.

LESSON 2 Classifying Numbers: Prime and Composite Numbers

Review It! When you classify numbers, remember these words:

prime number a number with exactly two factors, 1 and itself

composite number a number with more than two factors

3 is a prime number.

4 is a composite number.

Which of the following numbers is prime?

24, 27, 29, 49

Step 1 List the factors of each number.

> **REMEMBER** A factor divides a number evenly without a remainder.

24: 1, 2, 3, 4, 6, 8, 12, 24

27: 1, 3, 9, 27

29: 1, 29

49: 1, 7, 49

Step 2 Count the number of factors.

24 has 8 factors.

27 has 4 factors.

29 has _____ factors.

49 has _____ factors.

So, _____ is the prime number.

Try It! Write prime or composite for each number.

1. 28 _____   2. 5 _____   3. 31 _____

4. 17 _____   5. 33 _____   6. 9 _____

7. 23 _____   8. 12 _____   9. 100 _____

10. 16 _____   11. 81 _____   12. 103 _____

13. 125 _____ 14. 32 _____   15. 63 _____

16. 61 _____   17. 50 _____   18. 93 _____

19. 83 _____   20. 19 _____   21. 55 _____

1.

Is one of these a factor of 28? 2, 3, or 5?

4.

How many factors does a prime number have? 0, 1, or 2?

Solve.

22. The number of 5th-grade students in Saskia's school is a prime number greater than 50. What is the smallest number of 5th-grade students there could be?

_____

22.

Is one of these a factor of 51? 2, 3, 5, or 7?

23. Aaron visited India last year. The number of days he spent there is the largest two-digit prime number. How many days did Aaron spend in India last year?

_____

On Your Own!

Circle the best answer for each question.

1. Which is a prime number?

   A. 21

   B. 22

   C. 23

   D. 25

2. Which is a prime number?

   A. 37

   B. 39

   C. 56

   D. 57

3. Which is a composite number?

   A. 41

   B. 43

   C. 61

   D. 63

4. Which is a composite number?

   A. 101

   B. 103

   C. 105

   D. 107

5. Which is true about the number 45?

   A. It is composite because it has exactly two factors.

   B. It is composite because it has more than two factors.

   C. It is prime because it has exactly two factors.

   D. It is prime because it has more than two factors.

6. How many prime numbers are there that are between 20 and 30?

   A. 1

   B. 2

   C. 3

   D. 4

7. Find all of the prime numbers between 70 and 80.

_____

8. Show that 33,772 is a composite number.

_____

_____

Math Words | **Fill in the blanks.**

9. A number that has exactly two factors is a _____ number.

10. A number has more than two factors is a _____ number.

11. You know that 20 is a factor of 100 because there is no _____ when 100 is divided by 20.

12. If a number is prime, its factors are _____ and _____.

LESSON 3 — Divisibility Rules

 When you work with divisibility rules, remember this word:

divisible a number is divisible by a second number if the second number divides evenly into the first number

20 is divisible by 5 because 20 ÷ 5 = 4
20 is not divisible by 7 because 20 ÷ 7 = 2 R6.

Check whether 750 is divisible by 2, 3, 5, 9, or 10.

Step 1 Check the divisor 2.

750 is an even number. Every even number is divisible by 2. ◄···· **THINK** Even numbers end in 0, 2, 4, 6, or 8.

Step 2 Check the divisor 3.

To check 3, use this method:
Add the digits in 750: 7 + 5 + 0 = 12
Since 12 is divisible by 3, so is 750. ◄········ **THINK** This is the divisibility rule for 3.

Step 3 Check the divisor 5.

If a number's ones digit is 0 or 5, it is divisible by 5.

Step 4 Check the divisor 9.

To check 9, use this method:
Add the digits in 750: 7 + 5 + 0 = 12
Since 12 is not divisible by 9, 750 is not divisible by 9.

Step 5 Check the divisor 10.

If a number's ones digit is 0, it is divisible by 10.

So, 750 is divisible by _____, _____, _____, and _____.

 Find if each number is divisible by 2, 3, or 5.

1. 21 _____   **2.** 12 _____   **3.** 19 _____

4. 510 _____   **5.** 123 _____   **6.** 1,000 _____

7. 675 _____   **8.** 809 _____   **9.** 935 _____

Find if each number is divisible by 9 or 10.

10. 738 _____   **11.** 927 _____   **12.** 5,230 _____

13 60 _____   **14.** 743 _____   **15.** 85 _____

16. 315 _____   **17.** 3,450 _____   **18.** 621 _____

Solve.

19. The digits in a three-digit number are 9, 5, and 4. Use these digits to make a three-digit number that is divisible by 5 and by 9. _____

20. The smallest three-digit number is 100. What is the smallest three-digit number that is divisible by 3 and 10? _____

Ask Yourself

1.
What type of number is 21? Even or odd?

10.
What is the sum of the digits? 17, 18, 19?

19.
What must the ones digit be? 4, 5, 9?

On Your Own!

Circle the best answer for each question.

1. Which number is divisible by 3?

   A. 111

   B. 121

   C. 131

   D. 133

2. Which number is NOT divisible by 5?

   A. 95

   B. 500

   C. 505

   D. 551

3. 7,132 is divisible by –

   A. 2

   B. 3

   C. 5

   D. 9

4. Which number is NOT divisible by 9?

   A. 909

   B. 1,234

   C. 3,456

   D. 9,009

5. By which numbers is 762 divisible?

   A. 2, but not 3

   B. 3, but not 2

   C. both 2 and 3

   D. neither 2 nor 3

6. Mel's address on Oak Street is divisible by 3 and 5, but not by 9 or 10. Which of these could be Mel's address?

   A. 35 Oak Street

   B. 135 Oak Street

   C. 435 Oak Street

   D. 750 Oak Street

7. The largest three-digit number is 999. What is the largest three-digit number that is divisible by both 5 and 9?

   A. 995

   B. 990

   C. 985

   D. 980

8.   **Part A.**   Explain how you check to see if a number is divisible by 9.

_____

_____

Part B.   Use your method from Part A to test whether 58,734 is divisible by 9.

_____

_____

Math Words   **Fill in the blanks.**

9.   To use the _____ _____ for 5, look at the last digit of a number.

10.   Since there is no remainder when you divide 48 by 3, 48 is _____ by 3.

11.   Every _____ number is divisible by 2.

12.   A number is divisible by 10 if its _____ _____ is 0.

13.   A number is divisible by 3 if the _____ of its digits is divisible by 3.

Understanding Decimals and Place Value

Review It! When you work with decimals and place value, remember these words:

decimal a number with whole number places and places less than 1

decimal point a period used to separate the whole number places from the places less than 1 in a decimal

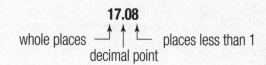

17.08

whole places ⟶ ↑ ↑ ↑ ⟵ places less than 1
decimal point

Write the number 234.615 in words.

Step 1 Make a place-value chart.

HUNDREDS	TENS	ONES	.	TENTHS	HUNDREDTHS	THOUSANDTHS
			.			

Step 2 Fill in the number from left to right.

HUNDREDS	TENS	ONES	.	TENTHS	HUNDREDTHS	THOUSANDTHS
2	3	4	.			

Read in the number from left to right.

Read the whole part first: *two hundred thirty-four.*

Read the decimal point as *and.*

Read the part to the right of the decimal point as *six hundred fifteen thousandths.*

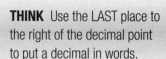

THINK Use the LAST place to the right of the decimal point to put a decimal in words.

So, 234.615 in words is _____

_____.

 **Write the number in words.**

1. 8.27 _____

_____

2. 124.6 _____

_____

3. 77.302 _____

_____

4. 15.009 _____

_____

1.

What is the last place to the right? Tenths, hundredths, or thousandths?

Write the number as a decimal.

5. forty and nineteen hundredths _____

6. five and five tenths _____

7. sixty and eight thousandths _____

8. nine and two hundred eleven thousandths _____

5.

How many places to the right of the decimal point should it go?

1, 2, or 3?

Solve.

9. Dean wrote a check for six hundred eight dollars and forty-seven cents. Write this amount as a decimal dollar amount. _____

10. The mixed number $3\frac{5}{8}$ is equivalent to the decimal 3.625. Write 3.625 in words. _____

9.

How many digits are there to the right of the decimal point in money amounts? 1, 2, or 3?

On Your Own!

Circle the best answer for each question.

1. Which digit is in the hundredths place of 304.287?

    A.   2

    B.   3

    C.   7

    D.   8

2. What is the value of the 5 in the number 7.522?

    A.   five hundredths

    B.   five oneths

    C.   five tenths

    D.   five thousandths

3. How is the number 40.27 written in words?

    A.   forty and twenty-seven hundredths

    B.   forty and twenty-seven tenths

    C.   forty and twenty-seven thousandths

    D.   four hundred two and seven tenths

4. How is the number *nine and nine thousandths* written as a decimal?

    A.   0.0018

    B.   0.018

    C.   9.0009

    D.   9.009

5. The mass of a crystal is thirty-five thousandths of a gram. How is this mass written as a decimal?

    A.   0.0035 grams

    B.   0.035 grams

    C.   0.35 grams

    D.   35,000 grams

6. A runner's time in a race was 17.890 seconds. How is this time written in words?

    A.   seventeen and eight hundred ninety hundredths

    B.   seventeen and eight hundred ninety thousandths

    C.   seventeen and eighty-nine tenths

    D.   seventeen and eighty-nine thousandths

7. Normal human body temperature is 98.6 degrees Fahrenheit.

    Part A.   How is this number written in words?

    _____

    Part B.   Explain the steps you used to write the word form in Part A.

    _____

    _____

    _____

Math Words   **Fill in the blanks.**

8. The period that separates the two parts of a decimal is called the _____
    _____.

9. The number to the left side of the decimal point is the _____ part of the
    number.

10. The first place to the right of the decimal point in a number is the _____
    place.

LESSON 5 — Multiplying and Dividing Decimals by a Whole Number

Review It! When you multiply and divide decimals by a whole number, remember these words:

dividend a number being divided

divisor the number you are dividing

quotient the result of division

$$100 \div 4 = 25$$

dividend divisor quotient

Find $15.25 \div 5$.

Step 1 Estimate.

15.25 is about 15, and $15 \div 5 = 3$.

Step 2 Write the division problem.

Place the decimal point in the quotient.

$$5\overline{)\,15.25}$$

REMEMBER Write decimal point directly above where it is in the dividend.

Step 3 Divide.

```
      3.05
  5) 15.25
    −15
      0 2
      −0
       25
      −25
        0
```

THINK Divide decimals just like whole numbers.

So, $15.25 \div 5 =$ _____

Find each quotient.

1. 31.44 ÷ 6 = _____   **2.** 12.238 ÷ 2 = _____

3. 87.75 ÷ 5 = _____   **4.** 2.538 ÷ 9 = _____

5. 44.8 ÷ 8 = _____   **6.** 16.142 ÷ 7 = _____

Ask Yourself

1.
Which is a good estimate? 0.5 or 5?

Find each product.

7. 5.23 × 6 = _____   **8.** 4.51 × 7 = _____

9. 1.013 × 9 = _____   **10.** 15.4 × 5 = _____

11. 19.33 × 4 = _____   **12.** 57.9 × 8 = _____

7.
How many decimal places will the product have? 1, 2, or 3?

Solve.

13. Kieran broke a multiplication problem into two parts. Here is what he wrote:

$$(2 \times 9) + (0.3 \times 9)$$

What was the original multiplication problem? _____

14. Jayna bought 8 packs of ribbon. Each pack cost $1.39. How much did Jayna spend in all? _____

13.
Which property does this remind you of? Commutative or Distributive?

On Your Own!

Circle the best answer for each question.

1. $7.5 \times 4 =$

    A. 11.5

    B. 28

    C. 28.5

    D. 30

2. $18.24 \div 6 =$

    A. 0.304

    B. 0.34

    C. 3.04

    D. 3.4

3. Which of the following is the same as 5.72×9?

    A. $(5 \times 9) + (0.7 \times 9) + (0.02 \times 9)$

    B. $(5 \times 9) + (0.7 \times 9) + (0.2 \times 9)$

    C. $(5 \times 9) + (7 \times 9) + (2 \times 9)$

    D. $(0.5 \times 9) + (0.7 \times 9) + (0.02 \times 9)$

4. $29.5 \div 5 =$

    A. 59

    B. 5.9

    C. 5.09

    D. 0.59

5. $24.05 \times 8 =$

    A. 19.204

    B. 19.24

    C. 192.04

    D. 192.4

6. Three pepperoni pizzas cost $38.25. How much does one pepperoni pizza cost?

    A. $12.25

    B. $12.75

    C. $13.25

    D. $13.75

7. Bree earns $7.50 for each hour babysitting. How much does Bree earn for 9 hours of babysitting?

    A. $16.50

    B. $63.50

    C. $67.50

    D. $72.50

8. Find each product.

$7.275 \times 10 =$ _____

$7.275 \times 100 =$ _____

$7.275 \times 1{,}000 =$ _____

9. Describe any pattern you see in the products from Question 8.

_____

_____

 Fill in the blanks.

10. The result of division is called the _____.

11. A number being divided by is called the _____.

12. When dividing a decimal by a whole number, write the decimal point in the quotient directly above the decimal point in the _____.

13. The result of multiplying two numbers is called the _____.

6 ⟩ Multiplying Decimals

Review It! Remember you can multiply decimals just like whole numbers

---

Find 24.6 × 0.34

Step 1 Multiply the numbers without their decimal points.

$$
\begin{array}{r}
24.6 \\
\times\ 0.34 \\
\end{array}
\qquad
\begin{array}{r}
246 \\
\times\ 34 \\
\hline
984 \\
7380 \\
\hline
8364 \\
\end{array}
$$

> **REMEMBER** Write a 0 in the ones place. Then find 246 × 3.

Step 2 Count the digits to the right of the decimal point in each factor.

24.6 has 1 digit to the right of the decimal point.

0.34 has _____ digits to the right of the decimal point.

In all, they have _____ digits to the right of the decimal point.

Step 3 Move the decimal point in your product.

24.6 and 0.34 have a total of 3 digits to the right of the decimal point. So, move the decimal point 3 digits to the left in 8,364.

8.364

> **THINK** 8,364 has its decimal point after the 4.

So, 24.6 × 0.34 = _____

 **Find the product.**

1. $2.5 \times 1.25 =$ _____   **2.** $5.8 \times 3 =$ _____

1.

How many decimal places will the product have? 1, 2, or 3?

3. $12 \times 3.44 =$ _____   **4.** $0.7 \times 0.4 =$ _____

5. $6.15 \times 4.6 =$ _____   **6.** $10.1 \times 1.1 =$ _____

7. $8.09 \times 320 =$ _____   **8.** $7.17 \times 4.98 =$ _____

9. $275 \times 8.08 =$ _____   **10.** $54.07 \times 3.7 =$ _____

Solve.

11. Naomi earns $15.60 per hour. If she works 6.25 hours today, how much will she earn? _____

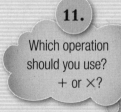

11.

Which operation should you use? + or ×?

12. The price of Regina cookies is $4.50 per pound. Thom bought 3.5 pounds of Regina cookies. How much did he spend? _____

On Your Own!

Circle the best answer for each question.

1. $18 \times 5.25 =$

   A. 90.25

   B. 94.25

   C. 94.5

   D. 945.0

2. $7.1 \times 6.01 =$

   A. 42.671

   B. 43.31

   C. 426.71

   D. 433.1

3. If you multiply 4.009 and 3.005, how many decimal places will there be in the product?

   A. 9

   B. 6

   C. 3

   D. 2

4. $8.16 \times 3.02 =$

   A. 24.6432

   B. 26.112

   C. 246.432

   D. 261.12

5. Paloma bought 450,000 shares of a stock selling for $0.003 per share. How much did Paloma spend in all?

   A. $135

   B. $1,350

   C. $13,500

   D. $135,000

6. Ham costs $7.50 per pound. Dan bought 4.5 pounds of ham for a party. How much did he spend in all?

   A. $12.00

   B. $27.50

   C. $29.00

   D. $33.75

7. Explain how counting digits to the right of the decimal point helps you multiply decimals.

_____

_____

8. Arni made a mistake multiplying 15.68 and 14.2. He wrote the product as 20.6976. How could counting decimal places have helped Arni?

_____

_____

Math Words | **Fill in the blanks.**

9. The _____ of 2.4 and 1.5 is 3.6

10. To multiply decimals, you can begin by multiplying _____ _____ instead.

11. The number 4.005 has _____ digits to the right of its decimal point.

12. If you multiply 12.89 and 23.176, the answer will have _____ digits to the right of its decimal point.

LESSON 7 — Dividing Decimals

Review It!   Remember to move the decimal points to make the divisor a whole number.

Find 151.9 ÷ 9.8.

Step 1   Estimate.

151.9 is about 150 and 9.8 is about 10. So, 151.9 ÷ 9.8 is about _____.

Step 2   Write the division problem.

$9.8\overline{)151.9}$

Step 3   Move decimal points in the divisor and dividend.

$98\overline{)1519}$ ◀┈┈┈┈┈┈   **THINK** Multiply 9.8 and 151.9 by 10.

Step 4   Solve.

```
        □ □ . □
 98)1 5 1 9 . 0         ◀┈┈┈┈  THINK Write 1,519 as
    9 8                        1,519.0 to finish dividing.
    5 3 9
    4 9 0
      4 9 0
      4 9 0
          0
```

So, 151.9 ÷ 9.8 = _____

Try It!   Find the quotient.

1. $36.4 \div 5.6 =$ _____

2. $675 \div 2.25 =$ _____

3. $208.38 \div 45.3 =$ _____

4. $7.92 \div 9.9 =$ _____

5. $7.5 \overline{)900}$

6. $7.81 \overline{)359.26}$

7. $2.2 \overline{)15.4}$

8. $41 \overline{)133.25}$

9. $2.03 \overline{)67.599}$

10. $3.14 \overline{)8.53452}$

Solve.

11. Kirsten drove 189 miles from Athens to her home. The drive took 3.5 hours. What was Kirsten's average speed, in miles per hour? _____

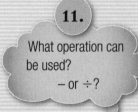

12. A 2.5-ounce jar of cinnamon costs $1.95. How much does 1 ounce of this cinnamon cost? _____

On Your Own!

Circle the best answer for each question.

1. $5.4 \div 0.6 =$

   A. 0.09

   B. 0.9

   C. 9

   D. 90

2. $5.58 \div 3.1 =$

   A. 0.16

   B. 0.18

   C. 1.6

   D. 1.8

3. $2.5 \overline{)72.5}$

   A. 2.7

   B. 2.9

   C. 27

   D. 29

4. $5.8 \overline{)12.76}$

   A. 0.22

   B. 2.2

   C. 22

   D. 220

5. A box of cereal weighs 11.25 ounces. There are 15 servings in the box. How much does 1 serving weigh?

   A. 3.75 ounces

   B. 1.33 ounces

   C. 0.75 ounces

   D. 0.075 ounces

6. It cost Steve $6.50 to park at the airport for 25 minutes. How much did it cost per minute to park?

   A. $0.26

   B. $0.25

   C. $0.026

   D. $0.025

Anita said that 63.427 ÷ 9.1 = 0.697. Use this information for Questions 7 and 8.

7. Explain how you can use estimation to show that Anita is wrong.

   _____

   _____

8. Show how to find the right answer.

 Fill in the blanks.

9. The _____ of 2.5 and 1.25 is 2.

10. In the number sentence 7.2 ÷ 6 = 1.2, 7.2 is the _____.

11. To solve $24\overline{)12}$, add a zero to the right of the _____ _____ in 12.

12. In the number sentence 8.4 ÷ 8 = 1.05, 8 is the _____.

LESSON 8 — Equivalent Fractions and Simplifying Fractions

Review It! When you work with equivalent fractions and simplify fractions, remember these words:

fraction a number used to name part of a whole or part of a group

numerator the number in a fraction above the bar

denominator the number in a fraction below the bar

equivalent fractions fractions that have the same value

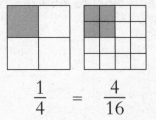

$$\frac{1}{4} = \frac{4}{16}$$

Find the fraction equivalent to $\frac{2}{3}$: $\frac{6}{10}$, $\frac{12}{16}$, or $\frac{12}{18}$.

Step 1 Simplify each of the three fractions.

$$\frac{6}{10} = \frac{6 \div 2}{10 \div 2} = \frac{3}{5}$$

$$\frac{12}{16} = \frac{12 \div 4}{16 \div 4} = \frac{\Box}{\Box}$$

$$\frac{12}{18} = \frac{12 \div \Box}{18 \div \Box} = \frac{\Box}{\Box}$$

THINK To simplify, divide the numerator and the denominator by their greatest common factor.

Step 2 Simplify $\frac{2}{3}$.

Since 2 and 3 share only 1 as a factor, $\frac{2}{3}$ is already simplified.

Step 3 Compare fractions to see which are equivalent to $\frac{2}{3}$.

So, only _____ is equivalent to $\frac{2}{3}$.

THINK A fraction that can't be simplified any more is in *lowest terms*.

Try It! Is the fraction in lowest terms?
Write Yes or No.

1. $\frac{4}{6}$ _____

2. $\frac{2}{10}$ _____

3. $\frac{1}{8}$ _____

1.
Do 4 and 6 both have 2 as a factor? Yes or No?

4. $\frac{5}{6}$ _____

5. $\frac{5}{25}$ _____

6. $\frac{2}{10}$ _____

7. $\frac{10}{20}$ _____

8. $\frac{7}{15}$ _____

9. $\frac{9}{16}$ _____

Write each fraction in lowest terms.

10. $\frac{6}{27}$ _____

11. $\frac{5}{24}$ _____

12. $\frac{12}{20}$ _____

10.
Which is a factor of both 6 and 27? 2, 3, or 9?

13. $\frac{3}{6}$ _____

14. $\frac{6}{15}$ _____

15. $\frac{15}{27}$ _____

16. $\frac{9}{12}$ _____

17. $\frac{3}{9}$ _____

18. $\frac{10}{18}$ _____

Are the fractions equivalent? Write Yes or No.

19. $\frac{1}{2}$ and $\frac{7}{14}$ _____

20. $\frac{4}{5}$ and $\frac{10}{12}$ _____

19.
Which is a factor of both 7 and 14? 2, 7, or 14?

21. $\frac{3}{4}$ and $\frac{15}{25}$ _____

22. $\frac{6}{9}$ and $\frac{16}{24}$ _____

Solve.

23. Tim divided a pizza into eight slices and ate two of them. In lowest terms, what fraction of the pizza did Tim eat? _____

23.
What is the numerator? 2, 6, or 8?

24. During the ten days of spring break this year, it rained on six days. In lowest terms, on what fraction of the days did it rain? _____

On Your Own! Circle the best answer for each question.

1. Which fraction is in lowest terms?

    A. $\frac{2}{12}$

    B. $\frac{3}{11}$

    C. $\frac{3}{12}$

    D. $\frac{5}{15}$

2. Which fraction is equivalent to $\frac{4}{9}$?

    A. $\frac{5}{10}$

    B. $\frac{6}{15}$

    C. $\frac{9}{20}$

    D. $\frac{12}{27}$

3. Which fraction is equivalent to $\frac{8}{12}$?

    A. $\frac{3}{4}$

    B. $\frac{10}{14}$

    C. $\frac{16}{20}$

    D. $\frac{16}{24}$

4. How is $\frac{24}{30}$ written in lowest terms?

    A. $\frac{4}{5}$

    B. $\frac{5}{6}$

    C. $\frac{8}{10}$

    D. $\frac{12}{15}$

5. Twenty of the 48 members of a glee club are boys. What fraction of the members are boys?

    A. $\frac{1}{2}$

    B. $\frac{1}{3}$

    C. $\frac{5}{12}$

    D. $\frac{7}{16}$

6. Of the first 42 Presidents of the United States, eight were born in Virginia. What fraction was born in Virginia?

    A. $\frac{1}{5}$

    B. $\frac{1}{6}$

    C. $\frac{4}{21}$

    D. $\frac{4}{17}$

7.   **Part A.**   Explain the steps you follow to write a fraction in lowest terms.

_____

_____

Part B.   Use your answer from Part A to write $\frac{24}{56}$ in lowest terms.

_____

8.   Find three different fractions that are equivalent to $\frac{9}{15}$.

_____

 Fill in the blanks.

9.   When a fraction can't be simplified any more, it is written in _____ terms.

10.   In the fraction $\frac{2}{11}$, 2 is called the _____.

11.   In the fraction $\frac{5}{8}$, 8 is called the _____.

12.   Fractions that have the same value are called _____ fractions.

LESSON 9 — Fractions as Division

Review It!

When you work with fractions as division, remember these words:

improper fraction a fraction whose numerator is greater than or equal to its denominator

$\frac{17}{8}$ is an improper fraction since $17 > 8$.

mixed number a number with a whole number part and a fraction part

$1\frac{3}{4}$ is a mixed number

Rewrite $\frac{17}{8}$ as a mixed number.

Step 1 Rewrite the fraction as division.

$$\frac{17}{8} = 17 \div 8$$

THINK Fraction = numerator ÷ denominator.

Step 2 Solve the division problem.

$$
\begin{array}{r}
\square \\
8\overline{)1\ 7} \\
-\underline{1\ 6} \\
1 \leftarrow \text{remainder}
\end{array}
$$

Step 3 Rewrite the quotient as a mixed number.

$$2\ R1 = 2\frac{1}{8}$$

THINK Remainder ⟶ numerator
Divisor ⟶ denominator

So, $\frac{17}{8} = $ _____.

Try It! Use division to write each fraction as a mixed number or whole number.

 **Ask Yourself**

1. $\frac{5}{2}$ _____

2. $\frac{11}{4}$ _____

3. $\frac{10}{3}$ _____

4. $\frac{22}{5}$ _____

5. $\frac{17}{6}$ _____

6. $\frac{48}{6}$ _____

7. $\frac{35}{3}$ _____

8. $\frac{70}{7}$ _____

9. $\frac{63}{8}$ _____

10. $\frac{64}{4}$ _____

11. $\frac{92}{5}$ _____

12. $\frac{81}{7}$ _____

13. $\frac{18}{11}$ _____

14. $\frac{19}{1}$ _____

15. $\frac{50}{3}$ _____

16. $\frac{45}{9}$ _____

17. $\frac{59}{8}$ _____

18. $\frac{22}{7}$ _____

Solve.

19. Sam cuts a board that is 53 inches long into four equal pieces. How long will each piece be? Write your answer as a mixed number. _____

20. To practice for a marathon, Ana ran 8 times around a reservoir. She ran a total of 13 miles. How far is the distance around this reservoir? Write your answer as a mixed number. _____

On Your Own!

Circle the best answer for each question.

1. How is $\frac{25}{6}$ written as a mixed number?

   A. $2\frac{5}{6}$

   B. $4\frac{1}{25}$

   C. $4\frac{1}{6}$

   D. $4\frac{5}{6}$

2. How is $\frac{71}{4}$ written as a mixed number?

   A. $17\frac{3}{4}$

   B. $17\frac{1}{4}$

   C. $17\frac{1}{71}$

   D. $7\frac{1}{4}$

3. Which two numbers are equivalent?

   A. $2\frac{1}{3}$ and $\frac{7}{2}$

   B. $\frac{30}{7}$ and $4\frac{2}{7}$

   C. $\frac{62}{5}$ and $10\frac{2}{5}$

   D. $1\frac{1}{2}$ and $\frac{2}{3}$

4. Which two numbers are NOT equivalent?

   A. $1\frac{5}{5}$ and 3

   B. $1\frac{4}{9}$ and $1\frac{3}{9}$

   C. $\frac{40}{9}$ and $4\frac{4}{9}$

   D. $2\frac{3}{5}$ and $\frac{23}{5}$

5. Vilma's locust tree grew nine feet in four years. How much did her tree grow each year, on average?

   A. $\frac{4}{9}$ ft

   B. $2\frac{1}{4}$ ft

   C. $2\frac{1}{9}$ ft

   D. 5 ft

6. A store's bookshelf is 24 inches wide. If it holds 9 copies of a new cookbook with no extra space, how wide is each copy?

   A. $\frac{9}{24}$ in.

   B. $2\frac{1}{4}$ in.

   C. $2\frac{1}{6}$ in.

   D. $2\frac{6}{9}$ in.

7. Simon rewrote $\frac{23}{7}$ as $3\frac{2}{23}$.

Part A. Explain what Simon did right and what he did wrong.

_____

_____

Part B. Show how Simon should have rewritten $\frac{23}{7}$.

_____

 Fill in the blanks.

8. $\frac{15}{4}$ is called an _____ _____ because $15 > 4$.

9. Fractions like $\frac{15}{4}$ can be rewritten as _____ _____.

10. To rewrite $\frac{15}{4}$, _____ its numerator by its denominator.

Modeling Multiplying and Dividing Fractions

Review It! When you are multiplying and dividing fractions, remember this word:

reciprocal for any fraction, its reciprocal is found by exchanging its numerator and denominator

$\frac{3}{10}$ and $\frac{10}{3}$ are reciprocals.

Find $\frac{3}{4} \div \frac{1}{8}$.

Step 1

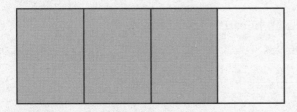

> **THINK** Shade 3 of the four rectangles to show $\frac{3}{4}$.

Step 2 Break the model into eighths.

$\frac{1}{8}$	$\frac{1}{8}$	$\frac{1}{8}$	
$\frac{1}{8}$	$\frac{1}{8}$	$\frac{1}{8}$	

Step 3 Count the shaded eighths in $\frac{3}{4}$.

There are _____ shaded eighths in $\frac{3}{4}$. So, $\frac{3}{4} \div \frac{1}{8} = 6$.

Step 4 Or, use the reciprocal.

> **THINK** To divide by a fraction, multiply by its reciprocal.

$$\frac{3}{4} \div \frac{1}{8} = \frac{3}{4} \times \frac{8}{1} = \frac{3 \times 8}{4 \times 1} = \frac{24}{4} = 6$$

So, $\frac{3}{4} \div \frac{1}{8} =$ _____

Try It!   Use the model to find the quotient.

1.
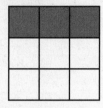

$\frac{1}{3} \div \frac{1}{9} =$ _____

2.
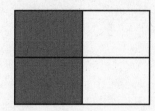

$\frac{1}{2} \div \frac{1}{4} =$ _____

Use the model to find the product.

3.
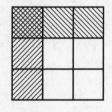

$\frac{1}{3} \times \frac{1}{3} =$ _____

4.
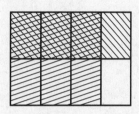

$\frac{1}{2} \times \frac{3}{4} =$ _____

Find each product or quotient.

5. $\frac{1}{2} \div \frac{1}{8} =$ _____

6. $\frac{1}{4} \times \frac{1}{4} =$ _____

7. $\frac{1}{2} \times \frac{1}{2} =$ _____

8. $\frac{5}{8} \div \frac{1}{8} =$ _____

9. $\frac{3}{5} \div \frac{1}{10} =$ _____

10. $\frac{3}{5} \times \frac{1}{3} =$ _____

Solve.

11.   Mrs. Lin served $\frac{1}{2}$ of a watermelon to her family. Her son ate $\frac{1}{3}$ of what Mrs. Lin served. What fraction of the whole watermelon did the son eat? _____

12.   A serving of trail mix weighs $\frac{1}{16}$ lb. A bag of trail mix weighs $\frac{3}{4}$ lb. How many servings are there in a bag?

_____

On Your Own!

Circle the best answer for each question.

Use the model to help answer
Questions 1 and 2.

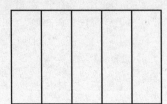

1. $\frac{3}{5} \times \frac{1}{2} =$

    A. $\frac{3}{10}$

    B. $\frac{3}{7}$

    C. $\frac{4}{7}$

    D. $\frac{4}{10}$

2. $\frac{4}{5} \div \frac{1}{10} =$

    A. $\frac{4}{50}$

    B.   8

    C.   10

    D.   40

3. What is the reciprocal of $\frac{7}{8}$?

    A. $\frac{7}{8}$

    B. $\frac{1}{8}$

    C. $\frac{1}{7}$

    D. $\frac{8}{7}$

4. $\frac{1}{4} \div \frac{1}{16} =$

    A.   4

    B.   12

    C. $\frac{1}{4}$

    D. $\frac{1}{64}$

5. José served $\frac{1}{2}$ of a pizza for lunch.
    Each of four friends ate $\frac{1}{4}$ of what
    José served. What part of the pizza
    did each friend eat?

    A. $\frac{1}{4}$

    B. $\frac{1}{6}$

    C. $\frac{1}{8}$

    D. $\frac{1}{16}$

6. One lap around a go-cart track is $\frac{1}{8}$
    of a mile. If Paige rode $\frac{1}{2}$ mile on this
    track, how many laps did she make?

    A.   2

    B.   4

    C.   6

    D.   8

7. **Part A.** How many quarters are there in a half-dollar?

_____

Part B. Show you can use a model to answer the question from Part A. Remember that a *quarter* equals one-fourth of a dollar.

Math Words **Fill in the blanks.**

8. When you divide $\frac{1}{6} \div \frac{1}{12}$, the dividend is _____.

9. The _____ of $\frac{5}{9}$ is $\frac{9}{5}$.

10. To divide $\frac{3}{4}$ by $\frac{3}{16}$, you can _____ $\frac{3}{4}$ and $\frac{16}{3}$.

11. The _____ of $\frac{1}{2}$ and $\frac{1}{2}$ is $\frac{1}{4}$.

LESSON 11 Greatest Common Factor (GCF) and Least Common Multiple (LCM)

Review It! When you find greatest common factors and least common multiples, remember these words:

greatest common factor (GCF) the largest number that is a factor of two or more numbers

least common multiple (LCM) the smallest number that is a multiple of two or more numbers

Find the GCF and LCM of 8 and 12.

Step 1 List the factors.

8: 1, 2, 4, 8

12: 1, 2, 3, 4, 6, 12

THINK Common factors of 8 and 12 are underlined.

Step 2 Find the GCF.

1 and 4 are common factors. So, the GCF of 8 and 12 is _____.

Step 3 List multiples.

8: 8, 16, 24, 32, 40, 48, …

12: 12, 24, 36, 48, 60, …

THINK Common multiples of 8 and 12 are underlined.

Step 4 Find the LCM.

24 and 48 are common multiples. So, the LCM of 8 and 12 is _____.

So, the GCF is _____ and the LCM is _____.

List the factors of each number.

1. 16 _____   **2.** 20 _____   **3.** 28 _____

Find the GCF.

4. 8 and 10 _____   **5.** 9 and 11 _____

6. 30 and 35 _____   **7.** 16 and 24 _____

8. 10 and 20 _____   **9.** 21 and 27 _____

Find the LCM.

10. 6 and 15 _____   **11.** 3 and 12 _____

12. 5 and 7 _____   **13.** 9 and 15 _____

14. 4 and 6 _____   **15.** 12 and 20 _____

Solve.

16. Hot dogs are sold in packages of 10 and hot dog buns are sold in packages of 8. Vincent bought the same number of hot dogs and buns. What is the least number of hot dogs Vincent could have bought? _____

17. To simplify the fraction $\frac{16}{36}$, Jasmine divided the numerator and the denominator by their GCF. What number did Jasmine divide by? _____

1.
Which is a factor of 16?
6, 8, or 32?

4.
Which is a factor of both 8 and 10?
2, 3, or 4?

10.
Which is a multiple of 6?
2, 3, or 12?

16.
Which do you use? GCF or LCM?

On Your Own!

Circle the best answer for each question.

1. What is the GCF of 20 and 25?

   A. 1

   B. 3

   C. 4

   D. 5

2. What is the LCM of 8 and 9?

   A. 1

   B. 36

   C. 48

   D. 72

3. What is the GCF of 16 and 24?

   A. 16

   B. 8

   C. 4

   D. 2

4. What is the LCM of 5 and 9?

   A. 45

   B. 15

   C. 14

   D. 1

5. The greatest common factor of Ferdy's age and Vyada's age is 6. What could their ages be?

   A. 24 and 32

   B. 12 and 18

   C. 6 and 20

   D. 2 and 3

6. Ceil is thinking of two numbers. Their least common multiple is 60. What could the numbers be?

   A. 6 and 10

   B. 8 and 10

   C. 10 and 12

   D. 20 and 40

7. A prime number has exactly two factors: 1 and the number itself. The numbers 73 and 127 are both prime numbers.

    Part A.   Find the GCF of 73 and 127.

    _____

    Part B.   Explain how you found the GCF of 73 and 127.

    _____

    _____

 Fill in the blanks.

8. 1, 2, 3, 4, 6 and 12 are the _____ of 12.

9. 7, 14, 21, 28, and 35 are _____ of 7.

10. The _____ _____ _____ of 6 and 9 is 3.

11. The _____ _____ _____ of 6 and 9 is 18.

LESSON 12 Finding Common Denominators

Review It!

When you are finding common denominators, remember these words:

common denominator a denominator that two or more fractions have

least common denominator (LCD) the smallest denominator that two or more fractions have (the LCM of the denominator)

Find the least common denominator for $\frac{3}{4}$ and $\frac{1}{6}$.

Step 1 List multiples for the two denominators.

4 has multiples 4, 8, 12, 16, 20, 24.

6 has multiples 6, 12, _____, _____.

> **THINK** $4 \times 1 = 4$, $4 \times 2 = 8$, and so on.

Step 2 Find the common multiples in the list.

4 and 6 have common multiples 12 and _____.

> **THINK** What numbers are in both lists?

Step 3 Find the least common multiple.

The least common multiple of 4 and 6 is _____.

> **THINK** LCD is just like LCM.

So, the least common denominator of $\frac{3}{4}$ and $\frac{1}{6}$ is _____.

Find the least common denominator for each pair of fractions.

1. $\frac{2}{9}$ and $\frac{1}{3}$ _____

2. $\frac{3}{4}$ and $\frac{5}{8}$ _____

3. $\frac{1}{5}$ and $\frac{5}{6}$ _____

4. $\frac{2}{3}$ and $\frac{2}{5}$ _____

5. $\frac{8}{9}$ and $\frac{1}{12}$ _____

6. $\frac{4}{5}$ and $\frac{7}{10}$ _____

7. $\frac{3}{7}$ and $\frac{3}{8}$ _____

8. $\frac{1}{2}$ and $\frac{1}{9}$ _____

9. $\frac{5}{6}$ and $\frac{5}{9}$ _____

10. $\frac{3}{8}$ and $\frac{9}{10}$ _____

11. $\frac{3}{5}$ and $\frac{7}{25}$ _____

12. $\frac{3}{4}$ and $\frac{11}{16}$ _____

13. $\frac{8}{11}$ and $\frac{1}{2}$ _____

14. $\frac{5}{8}$ and $\frac{5}{12}$ _____

15. $\frac{9}{10}$ and $\frac{4}{15}$ _____

16. $\frac{6}{7}$ and $\frac{1}{5}$ _____

17. $\frac{1}{6}$ and $\frac{5}{12}$ _____

18. $\frac{3}{10}$ and $\frac{5}{6}$ _____

Solve.

19. Cayden uses a common denominator to add the fractions $\frac{5}{6}$ and $\frac{7}{8}$. What are two different denominators that he could use? _____

20. Erin uses the least common denominator to subtract $\frac{1}{3}$ from $\frac{5}{6}$. What number will Erin use? _____

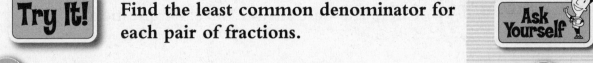

1.

Which is a multiple of both 3 and 9? 3, 6, or 9?

19.

What should you list?
Factors or multiples?

On Your Own!

Circle the best answer for each question.

1. What is the least common denominator of $\frac{3}{4}$ and $\frac{5}{7}$?

   A. 1

   B. 11

   C. 15

   D. 28

2. What is the least common denominator of $\frac{1}{10}$ and $\frac{7}{8}$?

   A. 18

   B. 40

   C. 60

   D. 80

3. Which is NOT a common multiple of 6 and 9?

   A. 36

   B. 48

   C. 72

   D. 90

4. What is the least common denominator of $\frac{7}{12}$ and $\frac{1}{8}$?

   A. 7

   B. 20

   C. 24

   D. 48

5. To add the fractions $\frac{1}{4}$ and $\frac{5}{6}$, Carl rewrites each using their least common denominator. What number does Carl use as his new denominator?

   A. 12

   B. 24

   C. 36

   D. 48

6. To subtract $\frac{3}{7}$ from $\frac{1}{2}$, Tanya first finds the least common denominator of the two fractions. Then she rewrites each fraction using the LCD as the denominator. How does Tanya rewrite $\frac{3}{7}$?

   A. $\frac{6}{14}$

   B. $\frac{5}{14}$

   C. $\frac{3}{14}$

   D. $\frac{4}{7}$

7.   Write the LCD for each pair of fractions.

$\frac{1}{6}$ and $\frac{1}{12}$ _____ $\frac{1}{6}$ and $\frac{1}{10}$ _____

$\frac{1}{5}$ and $\frac{1}{8}$ _____ $\frac{1}{5}$ and $\frac{1}{15}$ _____

$\frac{1}{4}$ and $\frac{1}{6}$ _____ $\frac{1}{4}$ and $\frac{1}{8}$ _____

8.   Look at your answers to Question 7. When does the LCD of two fractions equal one of the two denominators?

_____

_____

 Fill in the blanks.

9.   LCD stands for _____ _____ _____ .

10.   LCM stands for _____ _____ _____ .

11.   To find the LCD of $\frac{3}{14}$ and $\frac{5}{18}$, look at the numbers

_____ and _____ .

12.   To find an LCD, first list _____ of each fraction's denominator.

LESSON

LESSON 13 ▸ Comparing Fractions

Review It! Compare fractions by finding equivalent fractions with the same denominator.

Compare $\frac{2}{5}$ and $\frac{1}{3}$.

Step 1 Find a common denominator.

$$\frac{2}{5} = \frac{\blacksquare}{\square} \qquad \frac{1}{3} = \frac{\blacksquare}{\square}$$

THINK $5 \times 3 = 15$, so 15 is a common denominator.

Step 2 Write the equivalent fractions.

$$\frac{2}{5} = \frac{2 \times 3}{5 \times 3} = \frac{\square}{15}$$

REMEMBER Multiply the numerator and denominator by the same number to find equivalent fractions.

$$\frac{1}{3} = \frac{1 \times 5}{3 \times 5} = \frac{\square}{15}$$

Step 3 Compare. Write $>$, $<$, or $=$.

THINK The denominators are the same. Compare the numerators.

So, $\frac{2}{5} \bigcirc \frac{1}{3}$

Write a common denominator for each pair of fractions.

1. $\frac{2}{3}$ and $\frac{5}{9}$ _____

2. $\frac{7}{12}$ and $\frac{1}{8}$ _____

3. $\frac{5}{8}$ and $\frac{1}{4}$ _____

4. $\frac{2}{3}$ and $\frac{7}{12}$ _____

5. $\frac{1}{8}$ and $\frac{2}{10}$ _____

6. $\frac{1}{2}$ and $\frac{2}{5}$ _____

Compare. Write >, <, or =.

7. $\frac{4}{5}$ ◯ $\frac{2}{3}$

8. $\frac{3}{5}$ ◯ $\frac{6}{10}$

9. $\frac{3}{7}$ ◯ $\frac{5}{8}$

10. $\frac{2}{10}$ ◯ $\frac{3}{5}$

11. $\frac{7}{12}$ ◯ $\frac{3}{4}$

12. $\frac{1}{3}$ ◯ $\frac{2}{6}$

13. $\frac{3}{4}$ ◯ $\frac{9}{12}$

14. $\frac{1}{2}$ ◯ $\frac{5}{7}$

15. $\frac{4}{5}$ ◯ $\frac{7}{9}$

Solve.

16. Brody measured the growth of two plants. The bean plant grew $\frac{3}{8}$ inch, and the tomato plant grew $\frac{5}{12}$ inch. Which plant grew more?

_____

17. Did you know the world's two smallest lizards can each curl up on a dime? The Jaragua lizard is about $\frac{3}{5}$ inch long, and the Virgin Islands lizard is about $\frac{7}{10}$ inch long. Which lizard is the shortest?

_____

On Your Own!

Circle the best answer for each question.

1. Which symbol makes the sentence true?

$$\frac{3}{10} \bigcirc \frac{2}{5}$$

   A. $>$

   B. $<$

   C. $=$

   D. $+$

2. What is a common denominator of these fractions?

$$\frac{2}{3} \text{ and } \frac{3}{5}$$

   A. 6

   B. 8

   C. 12

   D. 15

3. Ramona wanted to run more than $\frac{5}{8}$ mile. Which distance is greater than $\frac{5}{8}$ mile?

   A. $\frac{3}{4}$ mile

   B. $\frac{1}{3}$ mile

   C. $\frac{2}{5}$ mile

   D. $\frac{7}{12}$ mile

4. Which symbol makes the sentence true?

$$\frac{4}{5} \bigcirc \frac{3}{4}$$

   A. $>$

   B. $<$

   C. $=$

   D. $+$

5. Which number sentence is true?

   A. $\frac{3}{5} > \frac{2}{3}$

   B. $\frac{4}{5} < \frac{2}{3}$

   C. $\frac{3}{4} < \frac{7}{8}$

   D. $\frac{3}{10} = \frac{3}{5}$

6. The Pacific Ocean covers a little more than $\frac{3}{10}$ of Earth's surface. The Atlantic Ocean covers less of Earth's surface than the Pacific Ocean. Which fraction shows the amount of Earth's surface the Atlantic Ocean covers?

   A. $\frac{1}{2}$

   B. $\frac{1}{5}$

   C. $\frac{3}{8}$

   D. $\frac{3}{4}$

7. Look at the fractions shown below.

$\frac{2}{5}$ $\frac{3}{8}$

Part A. Write the fractions with >, <, or = between them to compare.

_____

Part B. Explain how using equivalent fractions helped you compare the fractions. Use words and/or numbers in your answer.

_____

_____

_____

 Fill in the blanks.

8. I can use a _____ _____ of $\frac{4}{5}$ and $\frac{3}{4}$ to compare them.

9. The symbol > shows that $\frac{4}{5}$ is _____ _____ $\frac{3}{4}$.

10. $\frac{3}{4}$ and $\frac{15}{20}$ are _____ fractions because they are equal in value.

LESSON 14 Adding and Subtracting Fractions with Unlike Denominators

Review It! To add or subtract fractions, change fractions to the same denominator.

Scott drove $8\frac{3}{4}$ miles to a friend's house. Then he drove $1\frac{2}{3}$ miles to a park. How far did he drive altogether?

Step 1 Find the LCM of the denominators of $\frac{3}{4}$ and $\frac{2}{3}$.

Write the first 4 multiples of 4: 4, 8, 12, 16.

Write the first 4 multiples of 3: 3, 6, 9, 12.

The LCM is 12.

Step 2 Use the LCM to rename the two fractions.

$$\frac{3}{4} = \frac{3 \times 3}{4 \times 3} = \frac{9}{12}$$

REMINDER Multiply the numerator and the denominator by the same number.

$$\frac{2}{3} = \frac{2 \times 4}{3 \times 4} = \frac{\square}{\square}$$

Step 3 Write the mixed numbers using the renamed fractions.

$$8\frac{3}{4} = 8\frac{9}{12} \qquad 1\frac{2}{3} = 1\frac{8}{12}$$

REMINDER Only add the numerators of the fractions. Keep the denominators.

Step 4 Add the whole numbers. Then add the fractions.

$$8\frac{3}{4} + 1\frac{2}{3} = 8\frac{9}{12} + 1\frac{8}{12} = (8 + 1) + \left(\frac{9}{12} + \frac{8}{12}\right) = 9 + \frac{\square}{\square}$$

Step 5 Rewrite the mixed number.

$$9\frac{17}{12} = 9 + \frac{17}{12} = 9 + \frac{12}{12} + \frac{5}{12} = 10 + \frac{5}{12} = \underline{\hspace{2cm}}$$

So, Scott drove \underline{\hspace{2cm}} miles.

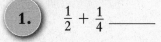 **Add.**

1. $\frac{1}{2} + \frac{1}{4}$ _____   **2.** $\frac{1}{6} + \frac{2}{3}$ _____   **3.** $\frac{3}{5} + \frac{3}{4}$ _____

4. $\frac{5}{6} + \frac{7}{8}$ _____   **5.** $4\frac{5}{8} + 2\frac{1}{2}$ _____   **6.** $1\frac{4}{5} + 2\frac{3}{8}$ _____

Subtract.

7. $2\frac{5}{8} - 1\frac{3}{4}$ _____   **8.** $\frac{5}{6} - \frac{2}{3}$ _____   **9.** $\frac{8}{9} - \frac{1}{6}$ _____

10. $1\frac{4}{5} - \frac{1}{2}$ _____   **11.** $1\frac{3}{16} - \frac{5}{6}$ _____   **12.** $4\frac{3}{10} - 1\frac{7}{8}$ _____

Solve.

13. A bean plant was $1\frac{5}{8}$ inches tall last week. Now it is $5\frac{1}{4}$ inches tall. How many inches did it grow?

_____

14. The art club ate $1\frac{5}{8}$ of a cheese pizza and $2\frac{2}{3}$ of a vegetable pizza. How much pizza did the art club eat in all?

_____

On Your Own!

Circle the best answer for each question.

1. Subtract: $\frac{3}{4} - \frac{11}{15}$

   A. $\frac{8}{11}$ C. $\frac{2}{15}$

   B. $\frac{1}{30}$ D. $\frac{1}{60}$

2. Add: $\frac{7}{8} + \frac{1}{6}$

   A. $1\frac{1}{24}$ C. $\frac{4}{7}$

   B. $1\frac{1}{48}$ D. $\frac{1}{3}$

3. Lisa spent $1\frac{3}{4}$ hours raking leaves yesterday and $\frac{5}{12}$ hour raking leaves today. How much time did she spend raking leaves yesterday and today?

   A. $2\frac{1}{2}$ hours

   B. $2\frac{1}{3}$ hours

   C. $2\frac{1}{4}$ hours

   D. $2\frac{1}{6}$ hours

4. Subtract: $10 - 2\frac{3}{5}$

   A. $8\frac{3}{5}$

   B. $8\frac{2}{5}$

   C. $7\frac{3}{5}$

   D. $7\frac{2}{5}$

5. Add: $4\frac{1}{3} + 2\frac{4}{5}$

   A. $6\frac{5}{8}$

   B. $6\frac{2}{15}$

   C. $7\frac{2}{15}$

   D. $7\frac{5}{8}$

6. A barrel holds 15 gallons of water. How much water is left after $5\frac{1}{8}$ gallons are poured out of the barrel?

   A. $9\frac{1}{8}$ C. $10\frac{1}{8}$

   B. $9\frac{7}{8}$ D. $10\frac{7}{8}$

7. Subtract: $6\frac{3}{4} - \frac{3}{8}$

   A. 6 C. $6\frac{1}{2}$

   B. $6\frac{3}{8}$ D. $6\frac{5}{8}$

8. Add: $18\frac{1}{2} + 7\frac{3}{5}$

   A. $25\frac{5}{7}$

   B. $25\frac{1}{10}$

   C. $26\frac{5}{7}$

   D. $26\frac{1}{10}$

9. Corey jogged $4\frac{5}{6}$ miles on Tuesday and $5\frac{3}{10}$ miles on Wednesday.

Part A. How much farther did Corey jog on Wednesday than on Tuesday?

_____

_____

_____

Part B. Show how you found your answer in Part A.

_____

_____

_____

_____

 Draw a line to match each word to its meaning.

10. least common multiple

the smallest denominator that two fractions can both have

11. least common denominator

the product of a number and a whole number

12. common denominators

a denominator that two fractions can both have

13. multiple

the smallest number that is a multiple of two or more numbers

LESSON 15 Fraction-Decimal Equivalencies

Review It! To write a fraction as a decimal, divide the numerator by the denominator.

Example 1 Write $\frac{7}{20}$ as a decimal.

Step 1 Divide the numerator by the denominator.

$$
\begin{array}{r}
0\,.\,3\ \ 5 \\
20\overline{)7\,.\,0\ \ 0} \\
-\ \Box\Box \\
\hline
1\ 0\ \ 0 \\
-\ \Box\Box\Box \\
\hline
0
\end{array}
$$

THINK Add 0s to the right of the decimal point in 7.

So, $\frac{7}{20} = $ _____.

Example 2 Write 0.16 as a fraction.

Step 1 Use place value to write a decimal as a fraction.

$$0.16 = \frac{16}{\Box}$$

REMEMBER Use the LAST place value to read a decimal number.

Step 2 Write the fraction in simplest form.

$$\frac{16}{100} = \frac{16 \div 4}{100 \div 4} = \frac{\Box}{\Box}$$

REMEMBER Divide by the greatest factor 16 and 100 both have.

So, $0.16 = $ _____.

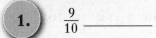 Write each fraction as a decimal.

1. $\frac{9}{10}$ _____   **2.** $\frac{13}{25}$ _____   **3.** $2\frac{7}{8}$ _____

4. $\frac{5}{16}$ _____   **5.** $8\frac{29}{40}$ _____   **6.** $\frac{4}{5}$ _____

7. $5\frac{1}{25}$ _____   **8.** $\frac{9}{20}$ _____   **9.** $\frac{33}{80}$ _____

Ask Yourself

1.

Which operation can you use?
$-$ or $\div$?

Write each decimal as a fraction in lowest terms.

10. 0.44 _____   **11.** 0.2 _____   **12.** 0.125 _____

13. 0.63 _____   **14.** 0.625 _____   **15.** 0.02 _____

16. 0.004 _____   **17.** 0.029 _____   **18.** 0.75 _____

10.

How do you read 0.44?
tenths or hundredths?

Solve.

19. A medicine has 0.375 milligrams of its active ingredient. Write this amount as a fraction in lowest terms. _____

20. A recipe uses $\frac{1}{4}$ teaspoon of pepper. Write this amount as a decimal. _____

19.

Which is a factor of both 375 and 1,000?
2, 3, or 5?

On Your Own!

Circle the best answer for each question.

1. How is $\frac{17}{100}$ written as a decimal?

   A. 17,100

   B. 1.7

   C. 0.17

   D. 0.017

2. How is $3\frac{9}{16}$ written as a decimal?

   A. 3.5625

   B. 3.565

   C. 3.916

   D. 4.778

3. How is 0.55 written as a fraction?

   A. $\frac{55}{1}$

   B. $\frac{55}{10}$

   C. $\frac{11}{25}$

   D. $\frac{11}{20}$

4. How is 0.024 written as a fraction?

   A. $\frac{1}{24}$

   B. $\frac{1}{41}$

   C. $\frac{1}{42}$

   D. $\frac{3}{125}$

5. A house for sale is on "a quarter of an acre" of land. How is this amount written as a decimal?

   A. 0.025 acre

   B. 0.25 acre

   C. 2.5 acre

   D. 25 acres

6. A piece of fabric is 0.875 yards long. How is this length written as a fraction?

   A. $\frac{7}{8}$ yard

   B. $\frac{5}{6}$ yard

   C. $\frac{4}{5}$ yard

   D. $\frac{3}{4}$ yard

7.   Pilar is using directions to find her friend's house. The directions read "After you make the right turn, drive $\frac{3}{4}$ of a mile."

   Part A.   Write this distance as a decimal.

   _____

   Part B.   Write $\frac{3}{4}$ as a decimal to the nearest tenth.

   _____

Use the fraction-decimal equivalence shown below to answer Questions 8–12.

$\frac{17}{20} = 0.85$

8.   The digit 5 is in the _____ place.

9.   The number 17 is in the _____ of the fraction.

10.   The digit 8 is in the _____ place.

11.   The number 20 is in the _____ of the fraction.

12.   The period between 0 and 8 is called the _____ _____.

LESSON 16 — Fractions: Estimating Products and Quotients

Review It! When you estimate, remember this word:

round to use a simpler estimate of a number

48.788 rounds to 50 $11\frac{3}{32}$ rounds to 11

Example 1 Is $\frac{1}{3} \times 23\frac{5}{8} = 8$ a reasonable estimate?

Step 1 Round the mixed number.

$23\frac{5}{8}$ rounds up to 24.   ◄········· **THINK** Round up since $\frac{5}{8} > \frac{1}{2}$.

Step 2 Estimate the product.

$$\frac{1}{3} \times 23\frac{5}{8} \approx \frac{1}{3} \times 24 = \frac{1}{3} \times \frac{24}{1} = \frac{1 \times 24}{3 \times 1} = \frac{\square}{\square} = \square$$

◄·· **REMEMBER** $\approx$ means is approximately equal to.

So, the estimate $\frac{1}{3} \times 23\frac{5}{8} = 8$ (is / is not) reasonable.

Example 2 Is $18\frac{1}{3} \div \frac{1}{2} = 9$ a reasonable estimate?

Step 1 Round the mixed number.

$18\frac{1}{3}$ rounds down to 18.

◄········· **THINK** Round down since $\frac{1}{3} < \frac{1}{2}$.

Step 2 Estimate the quotient.

$$18\frac{1}{3} \div \frac{1}{2} \approx 18 \div \frac{1}{2} = 18 \times \frac{2}{1} = \square$$

So, the estimate $18\frac{1}{3} \div \frac{1}{2} = 9$ (is / is not) reasonable.

Try It! Estimate each product. Show your work.

1. $\frac{1}{2} \times 29\frac{7}{8} \approx$ _____

2. $6\frac{4}{5} \times \frac{1}{7} \approx$ _____

3. $42\frac{2}{5} \times \frac{5}{6} \approx$ _____

4. $6\frac{1}{10} \times \frac{1}{2} \approx$ _____

5. $\frac{2}{9} \times 17\frac{1}{2} \approx$ _____

6. $\frac{1}{12} \times 23\frac{5}{8} \approx$ _____

7. $\frac{3}{4} \times 11\frac{1}{2} \approx$ _____

8. $19\frac{7}{8} \times \frac{4}{5} \approx$ _____

1.

$\frac{7}{8}$ ◯ $\frac{1}{2}$

<, =, or >

Estimate each quotient. Show your work.

9. $9\frac{4}{5} \div \frac{1}{5} \approx$ _____

10. $3\frac{1}{7} \div \frac{1}{6} \approx$ _____

11. $16\frac{5}{8} \div \frac{1}{2} \approx$ _____

12. $13\frac{1}{3} \div \frac{1}{3} \approx$ _____

13. $8\frac{5}{6} \div \frac{3}{4} \approx$ _____

14. $12\frac{1}{10} \div \frac{2}{5} \approx$ _____

15. $7\frac{3}{4} \div \frac{1}{2} \approx$ _____

16. $19\frac{3}{5} \div \frac{5}{7} \approx$ _____

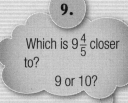

9.

Which is $9\frac{4}{5}$ closer to?

9 or 10?

Solve.

17. Melanie is hiking a trail that is $17\frac{3}{4}$ miles long. She wants to hike $\frac{1}{3}$ of the trail this morning. About how many miles will Melanie hike this morning?

_____

18. It took Jason $18\frac{3}{4}$ hours to build $\frac{1}{3}$ of a stone wall. About how long will it take Jason to build the whole wall?

_____

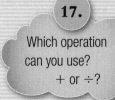

17.

Which operation can you use?

+ or ÷?

On Your Own!

Circle the best answer for each question.

1. Which is the most reasonable estimate of $21\frac{1}{4} \times \frac{1}{7}$?

   A. 3

   B. 4

   C. 5

   D. 6

2. Which is the most reasonable estimate of $15\frac{7}{8} \div \frac{1}{8}$?

   A. 2

   B. 22

   C. 120

   D. 144

3. Which is the best estimate of the quotient $20\frac{4}{5} \div 4$?

   A. a little less than 5

   B. a little more than 5

   C. a little less than 80

   D. a little more than 80

4. Which is the best estimate of the product $\frac{5}{6} \times 11\frac{5}{6}$?

   A. a little less than 2

   B. a little more than 2

   C. a little less than 10

   D. a little more than 10

5. A package of trail mix weighs $14\frac{1}{2}$ oz. Loris took $\frac{1}{5}$ of the trail mix to school each day. Which is the best estimate of the amount of trail mix Loris took to school each day?

   A. 2 oz

   B. 3 oz

   C. 4 oz

   D. 75 oz

6. Lita did $\frac{1}{4}$ of her project in $2\frac{3}{4}$ hours. Which is the best estimate of how long it will take Lita to do the entire project?

   A. 1 hour

   B. 3 hour

   C. 8 hours

   D. 12 hours

Chaz estimated the quotient shown. Use his work for Questions 7 and 8.

$$14\frac{2}{3} \div \frac{5}{7} \approx 14 \div \frac{5}{7} = \frac{14}{1} \times \frac{5}{7} = \frac{70}{7} = 10$$

7.   Describe any mistakes Chaz made.

_____

_____

8.   Estimate the quotient correctly. Show your work.

_____

_____

 Fill in the blanks.

9.   To divide by a fraction, multiply by its _____.

10.   To estimate $9\frac{5}{6} \div \frac{1}{4}$, first _____ $9\frac{5}{6}$ to 10.

11.   When you make a good estimate for a problem, that estimate is called _____.

12.   If you divide by a fraction between 0 and 1, the quotient will be _____ _____ the dividend.

Modeling and Applying Percents

Review It!

When you model and apply percents, remember these words:

circle graph a graph or pie chart used to show parts of a whole

percent a ratio of a number to 100

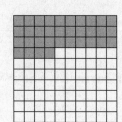 ← **Since 34 of 100 squares are shaded, 34% is shaded.**

Example 1 **Write 28% as a fraction in lowest terms.**

Step 1 Write the number of the percent in the numerator and 100 in the denominator.

$$28\% = \frac{28}{100}$$ ◀ **THINK** Percent means *per hundred.*

Step 2 Write the fraction in lowest terms.

$$\frac{28}{100} = \frac{28 \div 4}{100 \div 4} = \boxed{}$$ ◀ **REMEMBER** Divide by the GCF of 28 and 100.

So, 28% is written as a fraction is _____.

Example 2 **Write 28% as a decimal.**

Step 1 Rewrite the fraction as a decimal.

$\frac{28}{100}$ is read as 28 *hundredths*.

That means that $\frac{28}{100} = 0.$ _____ _____.

So, 28% is written as a decimal is _____.

Write the percent as a decimal.

1. 13% _____ **2.** 77% _____ **3.** 4% _____

Write the percent as a fraction in lowest terms.

4. 9% _____ **5.** 84% _____ **6.** 50% _____

Write the decimal or fraction as a percent.

7. 0.43 _____ **8.** $\frac{91}{100}$ _____ **9.** 0.6 _____

Use the circle graph to write the percent for each.

10. Win _____

11. Loss _____

12. No Decision _____

Toby's Pitching Results

Loss

Win

No Decision

Solve.

13. A real estate agent gets a 3% bonus when he sells a house. Write this percent as a decimal and as a fraction in lowest terms.

_____

14. DVDs are on sale for 25% off this week. Write this percent as a decimal and as a fraction in lowest terms.

_____

 **Ask Yourself**

1.
What goes in the denominator?
1, 10, or 100?

4.
Do 9 and 100 have any of the same factors?
Yes or No?

7.
In which place is the 3?
Tenths or hundredths?

10.
What fraction of the whole graph is Wins?
$\frac{1}{2}$, $\frac{1}{3}$, or $\frac{1}{4}$?

13.
What will the denominator be?
3, 10, or 100?

On Your Own!

Circle the best answer for each question.

1. How is 45% written as a decimal?

   A. 0.045

   B. 0.45

   C. 45.0

   D. 4,5000

2. How is 20% written as a fraction?

   A. $\frac{20}{1}$

   B. $\frac{2}{1}$

   C. $\frac{1}{50}$

   D. $\frac{1}{5}$

3. How is $\frac{11}{100}$ written as a percent?

   A. 1,100%

   B. 11%

   C. 1.1%

   D. 0.11%`

4. How is 0.9 written as a percent?

   A. 0.9%

   B. 9%

   C. 90%

   D. 900%

5. Some people were asked to name their favorite brand of cereal. The circle graph shows the results.

   Favorite Cereal Brands

   About what percent of the people chose Brand B?

   A. 60%

   B. 35%

   C. 30%

   D. 20%

6. An agent charges a rate of 0.06 to her clients. How is this rate written as a percent?

   A. 0.06%

   B. 0.6%

   C. 6%

   D. 60%

7. Paul needs to write the fraction $\frac{3}{4}$ as a percent. But $\frac{3}{4}$ does not have 100 as its denominator.

    Part A.   Show how you can change $\frac{3}{4}$ to a fraction with a denominator of 100.

    _____

    Part B.   Use your work from Part A to write $\frac{3}{4}$ as a percent.

    _____

 Fill in the blanks.

8.   A percent is a ratio of a number to _____.

9.   If you write 34% as a decimal, 3 goes in the _____ place and 4 goes in the _____ place.

10. _____ means *per hundred*.

11. If you write 7% as a fraction, the numerator is 7 and the _____ is 100.

12. Parts of a whole are shown on a _____ graph.

18 Estimating Areas

 **When you estimate area, remember these words:**

polygon a closed figure with straight sides   **area** the number of square units inside a figure

Estimate the area of the shaded polygon.

Step 1   Count the squares that are completely shaded.

There are 12 in all.   ◄ ············   **THINK** Count row by row.

Step 2   Count the squares that are exactly half-shaded.

Look at the bottom right side of the figure.

There are 4 half-shaded squares.

That makes 2 full square units.   ◄ ············   **THINK** $4 \times \frac{1}{2} = 2$.

Step 3   Count the other squares that are partly-shaded.

Look at the left side of the figure.

There are 6 squares that are partly-shaded. Some are a little less than half-shaded and some are a little more.

Estimate their total area: $6 \times \frac{1}{2} =$ _____ square units

Step 4   Add the partial areas.

12 + 2 + _____ = _____

So, an estimate of the shaded polygon's area is _____ square units.

Try It!

Estimate the area of each polygon.

1.

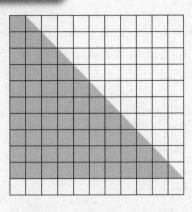

2.

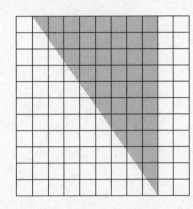

Ask Yourself

1.

How many squares are half-shaded? 6, 8, or 10?

3.

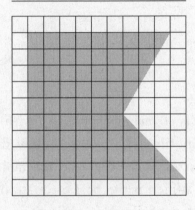

_____

4.

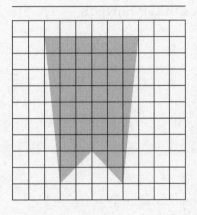

_____

Solve.

5.

Kayla is putting square tiles on a panel in her kitchen. The picture below shows the sizes of the tiles and the panel.

Tile   **Panel**

Estimate the number of tiles Kayla will need to cover the panel. _____

5.

How many tiles fit across the panel? 2, 3, or 4?

On Your Own!

Circle the best answer for each question.

Use the shaded polygon for Questions 1 and 2.

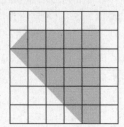

1. How many squares in the polygon are fully-shaded?

   A. 12

   B. 13

   C. 14

   D. 19

2. How many squares in the polygon are exactly half-shaded?

   A. 5

   B. 4

   C. 3

   D. 2

3. Which is the best estimate of the area of the quadrilateral?

   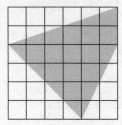

   A. 22 square units

   B. 18 square units

   C. 14 square units

   D. 10 square units

4. Ben is covering a table top with square tiles. The picture below shows the sizes of the tiles and the table top. Which is the best estimate of the number of tiles Ben will use?

   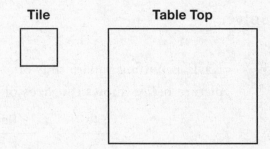

   A. 4 tiles

   B. 8 tiles

   C. 12 tiles

   D. 20 tiles

Use the triangle for Questions 5 and 6.

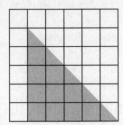

5. Derrick counted the half-shaded squares in the triangle. He estimated their total area as 3 square units. Explain how Derrick made his estimate.

_____

_____

6. Estimate the area of the triangle.

_____

 Draw a line to match each word to its definition.

7. area   a closed figure with straight sides

8. quadrilateral   the number of square units inside a figure

9. triangle   a three-sided figure

10. polygon   a four-sided figure

Measurement

LESSON 19 > Finding the Area of Parallelograms and Triangles

Review It! When you are finding the area of parallelograms and triangles, remember this word:

parallelogram a quadrilateral with two pairs of parallel sides

---

Find the area of the parallelogram.

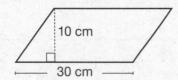

Step 1 Turn the parallelogram into a rectangle.

Cut off a right triangle along the altitude.

Then move the right triangle to the opposite side.

> **THINK** The altitude is a line segment used to measure height.

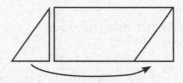

That creates a rectangle.

Step 2 Find the area of the rectangle.

> **THINK** The area of the parallelogram will be the same as the area of the rectangle.

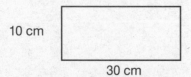

Area of rectangle = length × width = 30 × 10 = _____

So, the parallelogram has area of _____ sq cm.

Find the area of each parallelogram.

1.

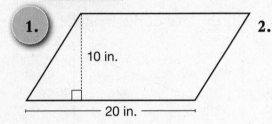

10 in.

20 in.

2.

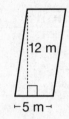

12 m

5 m

_____

_____

3.

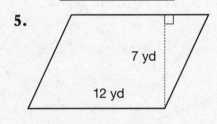

16 ft

11 ft

4.

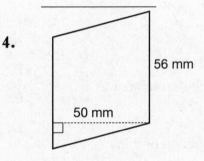

56 mm

50 mm

_____

_____

5.

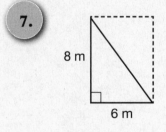

7 yd

12 yd

6.

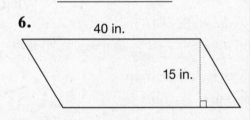

40 in.

15 in.

_____

_____

Find the area of each right triangle.

7.

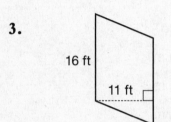

8 m

6 m

8.

 14 ft

5 ft

_____

_____

9.

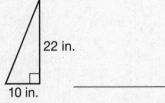

22 in.

10 in.

10.

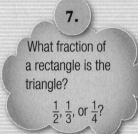

12 mm

12 mm

_____

_____

Measurement

Circle the best answer for each question.

Use the parallelogram for Questions 1 and 2.

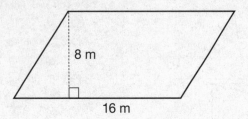

1. Which rectangle has the same area as the parallelogram?

   A.   a rectangle with length of 8 m and width of 8 m

   B.   a rectangle with length of 16 m and width of 16 m

   C.   a rectangle with length of 16 m and width of 8 m

   D.   a rectangle with length of 16 m and width of 4 m

2. What is the area of the parallelogram?

   A.   256 sq m

   B.   128 sq m

   C.   64 sq m

   D.   32 sq m

3. What is the area of the triangle?

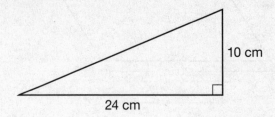

   A.   60 sq cm

   B.   120 sq cm

   C.   240 sq cm

   D.   480 sq cm

4. What is the area of the triangle?

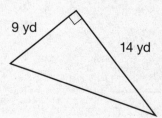

   A.   63 sq yd

   B.   66 sq yd

   C.   126 sq yd

   D.   252 sq yd

Measurement

Use the triangle for Questions 5 and 6.

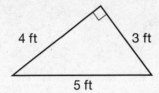

5. Kim wanted to find the area of the triangle. The first thing he did was multiply 5 and 4. Is Kim right? Explain.

_____

_____

6. Find the area of the triangle.

_____

 Fill in the blanks.

7. A parallelogram has two pairs of _____ _____.

8. To find the area of a parallelogram, you can replace it with a _____.

9. Units such as square inches and square feet are used to measure _____.

10. The area of a rectangle can be found using the formula

_____ × _____.

Measurement

Area of Triangles and Parallelograms

Review It! Remember to use formulas to find the area of polygons.

Find the area of each polygon.

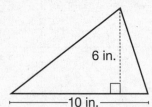
6 in.
10 in.

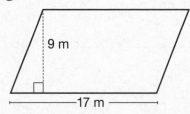
9 m
17 m

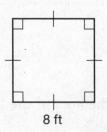
8 ft

Triangle Use the formula $A = \frac{1}{2}bh$ to find the area of a triangle.

b stands for *base* and h stands for *height*.

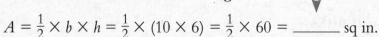

$A = \frac{1}{2} \times b \times h = \frac{1}{2} \times (10 \times 6) = \frac{1}{2} \times 60 = $ _____ sq in.

THINK The height starts at one vertex and meets the base at a right angle.

So, the area of the triangle is _____ sq. in.

Parallelogram Use the formula $A = bh$ to find the area of a parallelogram.

The height meets the base at a right angle, just like it does for a triangle.

$A = b \times h = $ _____ $\times$ _____ $= 153$ sq m.

THINK $A = bh$ is like the formula $A = lw$ for a rectangle.

So, the area of the parallelogram is _____ sq. m.

Square Use the formula $A = s^2$ to find the area of a square.

A square is a special type of parallelogram.

$A = s^2 = s \times s = $ _____ $\times$ _____ $= 64$ sq ft.

THINK s stands for side. s^2 means $s \times s$.

So, the area of the square is _____ sq. ft.

Try It!

Find the area of each polygon.

Measurement

1.

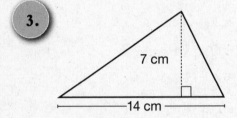

8 ft

5 ft

_____

2.

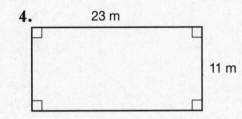

25 in.

_____

3.

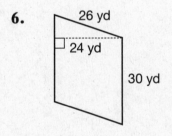

7 cm

14 cm

_____

4.

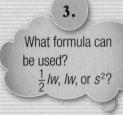

23 m

11 m

_____

5.

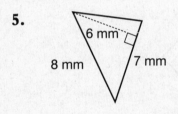

6 mm

8 mm   7 mm

_____

6.

26 yd

24 yd

30 yd

_____

7.

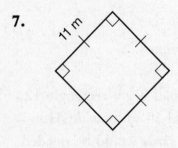

11 m

_____

8.

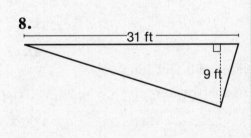

31 ft

9 ft

_____

Circle the best answer for each question.

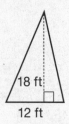

1. What is the area of the rectangle?

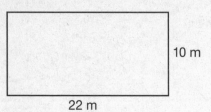

10 m

22 m

A. 32 sq m

B. 64 sq m

C. 110 sq m

D. 220 sq m

2. What is the area of the triangle?

18 ft

12 ft

A. 30 sq ft

B. 98 sq ft

C. 108 sq ft

D. 216 sq ft

3. Each side of a square is 50 feet long. What is the area of the square?

A. 2,500 sq ft

B. 1,250 sq ft

C. 250 sq ft

D. 200 sq ft

4. What is the area of the parallelogram?

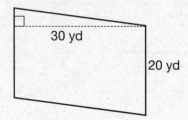

30 yd

20 yd

A. 1,200 sq yd

B. 600 sq yd

C. 300 sq yd

D. 60 sq yd

5. What is the area of the square?

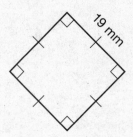

19 mm

A. 38 sq mm

B. 76 sq mm

C. 180.5 sq mm

D. 361 sq mm

6. A field is shaped like a rectangle 120 yards long and 50 yards wide. How many square yards would be needed to cover this field?

A. 6,000   **C.** 600

B. 3,000   **D.** 300

Measurement

7.   Explain how the formulas for the area of a triangle and the area of a parallelogram are alike and different.

_____

_____

8.   Explain how the formulas for the area of a square and the area of a rectangle are alike and different.

_____

_____

 Fill in the blanks.

9.   Area is measured in _____ units.

10.   A figure with two pairs of parallel sides is a _____.

11.   The formula $A = \frac{1}{2}bh$ can be used to find the area of a _____.

12.   A figure with four right angles and four congruent sides is a _____.

Measurement

LESSON 21 Area of Circles

 **Review It!** When you are finding the area of a circle, remember these words:

circle a closed figure with all points on the circle the same distance from its center

center the point in the middle of a circle that is the same distance from all points on the circle

radius a line segment from the center of a circle to any point on the circle

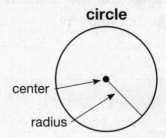

circle

center

radius

The radius of the circle above is 8 mm long. Find the area of the circle.

Step 1 Write the area formula for a circle.

$$A = \pi r^2$$ ◄······················ **REMEMBER** r^2 means $r \times r$.

π is a Greek letter. It stands for a number that is about 3.14.

r stands for the length of a radius.

Step 2 Replace π with 3.14 and r with the length of the radius, 8.

$A = \pi r^2$

$A = \pi \times r \times r$

$A = 3.14 \times 8 \times 8$

$A = 3.14 \times$ _____

$A =$ _____

So, the area of the circle is about _____ sq mm.

Find the area of each circle. Use 3.14 for π.

Measurement

1.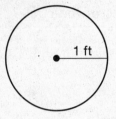

1 ft

_____

1.

What is 1²? 1, 2, or ½?

2.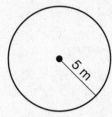

5 m

_____

3.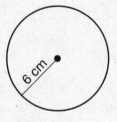

6 cm

_____

4.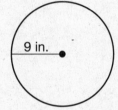

9 in.

_____

5.

17 mm

_____

6.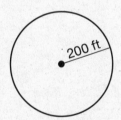

200 ft

_____

Solve. Use 3.14 for π.

7. Dewey has a circular swimming pool in his yard. The distance from the center of the pool to the wall is 10 feet, and the height of the pool is 4 feet. What is the area of the pool's surface? _____

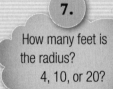

7.

How many feet is the radius? 4, 10, or 20?

8. The radius of a coin is 1.5 centimeters long. Find the area of the front of the coin, to the nearest whole number of square centimeters. _____

On Your Own! Circle the best answer for each question.

1. What is the area of the circle?

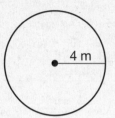

4 m

- **A.** 16 sq m
- **B.** 25.12 sq m
- **C.** 50.24 sq m
- **D.** 100.48 sq m

2. What is the area of the circle?

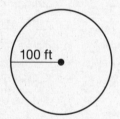

100 ft

- **A.** 314 sq ft
- **B.** 31,400 sq ft
- **C.** 314,000 sq ft
- **D.** 3,140,000 sq ft

3. A sprinkler waters a circle with a 20-foot-long radius. What is the area of the circle watered by this sprinkler?

- **A.** 40 sq ft
- **B.** 125.6 sq ft
- **C.** 400 sq ft
- **D.** 1,256 sq ft

4. What is the area of the circle?

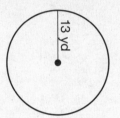

13 yd

- **A.** 1,061.32 sq yd
- **B.** 530.66 sq yd
- **C.** 265.33 sq yd
- **D.** 81.64 sq yd

5. A small pizza has a radius of 4 inches. A large pizza has a radius of 8 inches. Which sentence about the two pizzas is true?

- **A.** The large pizza has area four times as great as the small pizza.
- **B.** The large pizza has area twice as great as the small pizza.
- **C.** The large pizza has area 16 square inches greater than the small pizza.
- **D.** The large pizza has area 4 square inches greater than the small pizza.

6. Draw and shade a circle with radius of 3 units on the square grid.

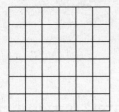

7. Show how to find the area OUTSIDE of the circle on the square grid.

_____

_____

  Fill in the blanks.

8. A circle is a closed figure with all points on the circle the same _____ from its center.

9. The point in the middle of a circle is called its _____.

10. The Greek letter _____ stands for a number that is about 3.14.

11. To find the area of a circle, you must measure the length of its _____.

Area of Composite Figures

Review It! When you find area of composite figures, remember this word:

composite figure a figure that can be divided into shapes you know

Here is a drawing of a playground. Find its area.

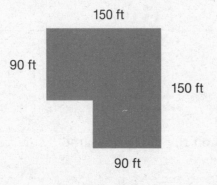

150 ft

90 ft

150 ft

THINK Do you see rectangles or squares?

Step 1 Look for shapes in the figure whose area you can find. ◄......

Step 2 Break the figure into parts. Draw a line to form two rectangles.

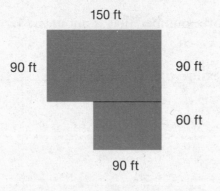

150 ft

90 ft

90 ft

60 ft

90 ft

THINK Area = length × width.

Step 3 Find the area of each rectangle. ◄......

The area of the top rectangle is 150 × 90 = _____ sq ft.

The area of the bottom rectangle is 90 × 60 = _____ sq ft.

So, the area of the playground is _____ sq ft.

Try It!   Find the area of each composite figure.

Ask Yourself

1.

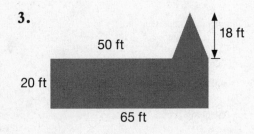

2.

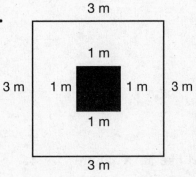

1.

What is the area of a triangle?
bh or $\frac{1}{2}bh$?

Measurement

3.

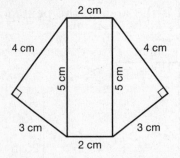

4.

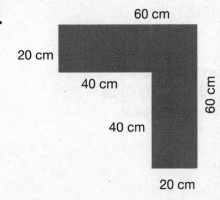

Solve.

5.   Val is using square tiles to cover her kitchen floor. A picture of the floor is shown below.

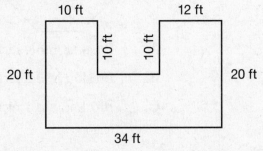

If each tile is 1 square foot, how many tiles will Val use?

5.

How many rectangles should you break the floor into?
3 or 4?

On Your Own!   Circle the best answer for each question.

1. What is the area of the composite figure below?

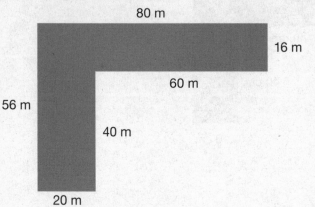

80 m

16 m

60 m

56 m

40 m

20 m

A. 2,080 sq m

B. 2,400 sq m

C. 2,480 sq m

D. 6,880 sq m

2. A garden is shaped like an X. There is a right angle at each corner of the garden and each side of the garden measures 40 feet long. What is the area of this garden?

A. 6,400 sq ft

B. 8,000 sq ft

C. 9,600 sq ft

D. 11,200 sq ft

3. What is the area of the pentagon below?

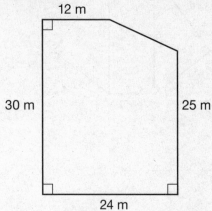

12 m

30 m

25 m

24 m

A. 750 sq m

B. 720 sq m

C. 690 sq m

D. 660 sq m

4. Ariel is using sheet metal to make a sign shaped like the octagon below. To find its area, she divides the figure into shapes she knows. Which of the following could Ariel do?

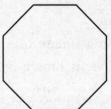

A. Break it into 4 rectangles.

B. Break it into 2 rectangles.

C. Break it into 1 rectangle and 2 triangles.

D. Break it into 5 rectangles and 4 triangles.

5. A strategy that is used a lot in mathematics to solve difficult problems is called *Solve a Simpler Problem*. Explain in your own words how this strategy could be used to explain how you find the area of a composite figure.

_____

_____

_____

 Fill in the blanks.

6. If a rectangle has sides measured in millimeters, its area will be measured in _____ _____.

7. A figure that can be broken down into shapes you know is a _____ _____.

8. The formula for the area of a triangle is _____.

9. The formula for the area of a rectangle is _____.

Measurement

LESSON 23 Measuring Capacity

 **Review It!** When you measure capacity, remember this word:

capacity the amount a container can hold

CONVERSION TABLES	
CUSTOMARY UNITS	**METRIC UNITS**
1 cup (c) = 8 fluid ounces (fl oz)	1 liter (L) = 1,000 milliliters (mL)
1 pint (pt) = 2 cups (c)	
1 quart (qt) = 2 pints (pt)	
1 gallon (gal) = 4 quarts (qt)	

Example 1 Use the table to convert 20 quarts to gallons.

Step 1 Divide to convert quarts to gallons.

20 qt = (20 ÷ 4) gal = 5 gal   ◄········· **THINK** Divide when you convert to a larger unit.

So, 20 quarts = _____ gallons.

Example 2 Use the table to convert 20 quarts to pints.

Step 1 Multiply to convert quarts to pints.

20 qt = (20 × 2) pt = _____ pt   ◄········· **THINK** Multiply when you convert to a smaller unit.

So, 20 quarts = _____ pints.

Try It! Convert each metric measurement.

 1. 2,000 mL = _____ L **2.** 15 L = _____ mL

3. 0.65 L = _____ mL

Convert each customary measurement.

4. 9 pt = _____ c **5.** 24 fl oz = _____ c

6. 15 gal = _____ qt **7.** 32 pt = _____ qt

8. 108 c = _____ pt **9.** 10 c = _____ fl oz

10. 10 qt = _____ gal **11.** 7 pt = _____ qt

12. 49 qt = _____ pt **13.** 64 fl oz = _____ c

14 2.5 gal = _____ qt **15.** $\frac{1}{2}$ qt = _____ pt

Solve.

16. Roddy tries to drink 1 cup of water 8 times each day. How many pints of water does Roddy try to drink each day? _____

17. Guava juice is sold in a 0.25-liter bottle. How many milliliters of guava juice are in this bottle? _____

Ask Yourself

1.
How many mL are in 1 L?
10, 100, or 1,000?

4.
How do you convert to a smaller unit? Multiply or divide?

16.
How many cups are in 1 pint?
2, 4, or 8?

Measurement

Circle the best answer for each question.

1. 8 pt = _____ qt

    A. 2

    B. 4

    C. 16

    D. 32

2. 4 cups = _____ fluid ounces

    A. 1

    B. 2

    C. 16

    D. 32

3. A jar of olive oil holds 0.7 liters. How is the jar's capacity written in milliliters?

    A. 7 mL

    B. 70 mL

    C. 700 mL

    D. 7,000 mL

4. 9,000 mL = _____ L

    A. 9

    B. 90

    C. 900

    D. 9,000,000

5. 40 qt = _____ gal

    A. 160

    B. 80

    C. 20

    D. 10

6. Dwayne buys 12 pints of juice. He pours the juice into 1-cup servings. How many servings can Dwayne pour?

    A. 48

    B. 24

    C. 6

    D. 3

Measurement

7. **Part A.** Complete the statements:

1 quart = _____ cups

1 gallon = _____ cups

Part B. Explain how you found your answers in Part A.

_____

_____

 Fill in the blanks.

8. The amount a container can hold is called its _____.

9. Milliliter and liter are _____ units of measurement.

10. Quart and cup are _____ units of measurement.

11. The abbreviation for fluid ounce is _____ _____.

Measurement

LESSON 24

Introduction to Volume of Prisms

Review It! When you are finding volume, remember these words:

rectangular prism a solid figure with all faces shaped like rectangles

volume a measure of the space enclosed by a three-dimensional figure

Find the volume of the rectangular prism in cubic centimeters.

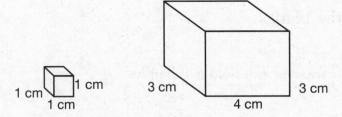

Step 1 Place one layer of cubic centimeters in the prism.

The bottom layer holds 12 cubic centimeters.

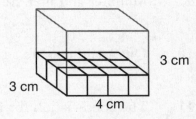

> **THINK** Since $A = lw$, there are 4×3 cubes on the bottom layer.

Step 2 Build each layer until the rectangular prism is full.

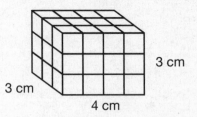

There are _____ layers of cubes in all.

Each layer holds _____ cubic centimeters.

So, the volume of the prism is _____ cubic centimeters.

> **THINK** The prism's height tells you how many layers there are.

In each picture, 1-inch cubes fill the bottom layer of a rectangular prism. Find the number of cubic inches that fill the bottom of each prism.

Ask Yourself

1.

Which area formula can help you? s^2, lw, or $\frac{1}{2}bh$?

1.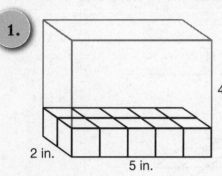

4 in.

2 in.

5 in.

2.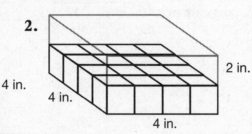

2 in.

4 in.

4 in.

_____   _____

3.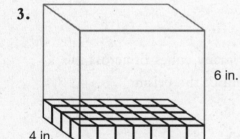

6 in.

4 in.

7 in.

4.

5 in.

6 in.

9 in.

_____   _____

Use the figures shown above to fill in the blanks.

5. The prism from Question 1 has a volume of _____ cubic inches.

5.

How many layers are there? 2, 4, or 5?

6. The prism from Question 2 has a volume of _____ cubic inches.

7. The prism from Question 3 has a volume of _____ cubic inches.

8. The prism from Question 4 has a volume of _____ cubic inches.

On Your Own!

Circle the best answer for each question.

1. Which unit can be used to measure the volume of a rectangular prism?

   A. centimeter

   B. cubic foot

   C. pound

   D. square inch

2. What does volume measure?

   A. the length of a two-dimensional figure

   B. the length of a three-dimensional figure

   C. the space enclosed by a two-dimensional figure

   D. the space enclosed by a three-dimensional figure

3. What is the figure shown called?

   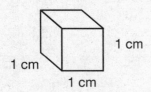

   1 cm

   1 cm

   1 cm

   A. centimeter

   B. cubic centimeter

   C. square

   D. square centimeter

Use the prism for Questions 4 and 5.

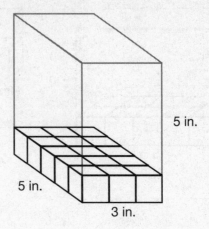

5 in.

5 in.

3 in.

4. How many cubes fit across the bottom of the prism?

   A. 15

   B. 13

   C. 11

   D. 7

5. Suppose the prism is filled with cubes like the ones shown. How many cubes will be used to completely fill the prism?

   A. 35

   B. 60

   C. 75

   D. 90

6. Explain what a cubic inch is.

_____

_____

7. Explain what it means for a prism to have a volume of 60 cubic inches.

_____

_____

Math Words

Fill in the blanks.

8. A rectangular prism is a solid figure with all faces shaped like _____.

9. Volume is a measure of the _____ enclosed by a three-dimensional figure.

10. A cube in which each side is 1 inch long is called a _____ _____.

11. Volume is measured in _____ units.

Measurement

Volume of Rectangular Prisms and Cubes

Review It! Remember to use the formula $V = l \times w \times h$ to find the volume of a rectangular prism.

Measurement

Find the volume of the rectangular prism.

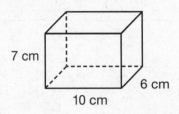

7 cm

6 cm

10 cm

Step 1 Write the volume formula.

$V = l \times w \times h$ ◄········· **THINK** l = length, w = width, and h = height.

Step 2 Substitute for $l, w,$ and h.

$V = 10$ cm $\times$ _____ cm $\times 7$ cm

Step 3 Find V.

$V = 10 \times 6 \times 7$ cm^3

$V =$ _____ cm^3 ◄········· **REMEMBER** Volume is measured in *cubic* units like cm^3.

So, the volume of the rectangular prism is _____.

Try It! Find the volume of each rectangular prism.

1.

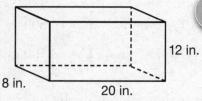

2 ft   8 ft
5 ft

_____

2.

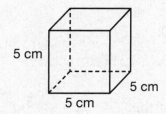

4 m
5 m   13 m

_____

Ask Yourself

1.

What unit can you use?
ft, ft², or ft³?

3.

12 in.
8 in.   20 in.

_____

4.

5 cm
5 cm
5 cm

_____

4.

What is the volume formula for a cube?
s^3, $3s$, or $6s$?

5.

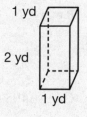

1 yd
2 yd
1 yd

_____

6.

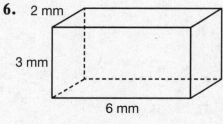

2 mm
3 mm
6 mm

_____

7.

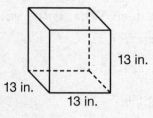

13 in.
13 in.
13 in.

_____

8.

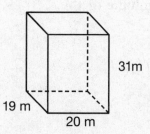

31m
19 m   20 m

_____

Circle the best answer for each question.

Measurement

1. What is the volume of the rectangular prism?

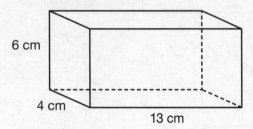

A. 23 cm³   **C.** 312 cm³

B. 23 cm²   **D.** 312 cm²

2. What is the volume of the rectangular prism?

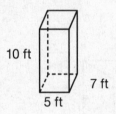

A. 35 ft³   **C.** 3,500 ft³

B. 350 ft³   **D.** 35,000 ft³

3. A sits on top of a base shaped like a cube. Each side of the base is 3 feet long. What is the volume of the base?

A. 9 ft³

B. 27 ft³

C. 54 ft³

D. 81 ft³

4. Which is the BEST ESTIMATE of the volume of the cube?

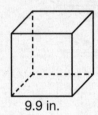

A. 1,000 in.³   **C.** 500 in.³

B. 700 in.³   **D.** 100 in.³

5. What is the volume of the rectangular prism?

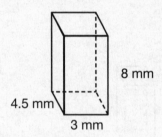

A. 124 mm³   **C.** 108 mm³

B. 120 mm³   **D.** 96 mm³

6. A freezer shaped like a rectangular prism is 180 cm long, 90 cm wide, and 60 cm deep. What is the volume of the freezer?

A. 330 cm³

B. 9,720 cm³

C. 97,200 cm³

D. 972,000 cm³

7. Renata and Paul each measured the same cube to find its volume. Renata found that each edge of the cube was 1 foot long. Paul found that each edge of the cube was 12 inches long.

   Part A.   What is the volume that Renata found?

   _____

   Part B.   What is the volume that Paul found?

   _____

   Part C.   Can Renata and Paul both be right? Explain why or why not.

   _____

   _____

 Fill in the blanks.

8. To find the volume of a rectangular prism, multiply its _____, _____, and _____.

9. If each side of a rectangular prism is measured in cm, its volume will be measured in _____.

10. If each edge of a cube measures s, you can find its volume using the formula $V =$ _____.

Review It! When you work with congruent figures, remember these words and symbols:

congruent figures figures with the same shape and the same size $\cong$ **is congruent to**

Find the triangle that is congruent to triangle *ABC*.

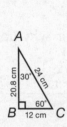
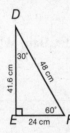

Step 1   Compare triangles *ABC* and *DEF*.

Congruent triangles must have matching congruent angles:

$\angle A \cong \angle D$ $\angle B \cong \angle E$ $\angle C \cong \angle F$ ◄·············

> **THINK** These are called corresponding angles. The symbol $\cong$ means "is congruent to."

Congruent triangles must have matching congruent sides:

$\overline{AB} \not\cong \overline{DE}$ $\overline{BC} \not\cong \overline{EF}$ $\overline{AC} \not\cong \overline{DF}$

So, triangles *ABC* and *DEF* are _____ _____.

Step 2   Compare triangles *ABC* and *XYZ*.

Check the angles:

$\angle A \cong \angle X$ $\angle B \cong \angle Y$ $\angle C \cong \angle Z$

Check the sides:

$\overline{AB} \cong \overline{XY}$ $\overline{BC} \cong \overline{YZ}$ $\overline{AC} \cong \overline{XZ}$ ◄········

> **THINK** These are called corresponding sides.

So, triangles *ABC* and *XYZ* are _____.

So, triangle *ABC* $\cong$ _____.

Geometry

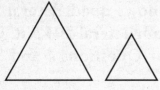

Do the triangles appear congruent? Write Yes or No.

1.

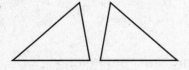

_____

2.

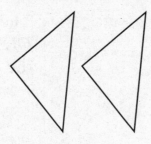

1.

Do matching sides appear— congruent or not congruent?

3.

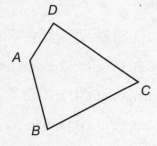

_____

4.

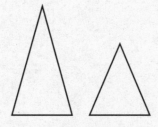

_____

The picture below shows quadrilateral $ABCD \cong$ quadrilateral $XYZW$. Use the picture to fill in the blanks.

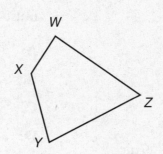

5. $\overline{AB} \cong$ _____

6. $\angle W \cong$ _____

7. $\overline{ZY} \cong$ _____

8. $\angle B \cong$ _____

9. $\overline{CD} \cong$ _____

10. $\angle Z \cong$ _____

5.

What does $\overline{AB}$ mean? Segment AB or angle AB?

Geometry

Circle the best answer for each question.

1. Which triangles are congruent?

A.

B.

C.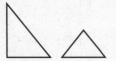

D.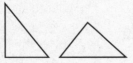

2. Triangle $ABC \cong$ triangle XYZ. Which angle must be congruent to angle B?

A. angle A

B. angle B

C. angle Y

D. angle Z

3. Triangle $KLM \cong$ triangle JVF. Which side must be congruent to $\overline{JF}$?

A. $\overline{KL}$

B. $\overline{KM}$

C. $\overline{LM}$

D. $\overline{VF}$

The picture shows quadrilateral $GHTQ \cong$ quadrilateral $PWNR$. Use the picture for Questions 4 and 5.

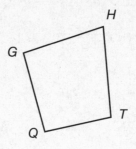 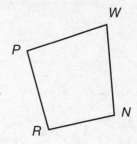

4. Which are corresponding angles?

A. $\angle H$ and $\angle R$

B. $\angle P$ and $\angle H$

C. $\angle Q$ and $\angle N$

D. $\angle H$ and $\angle W$

5. If the length of $\overline{TQ}$ is 5 m, what must be true?

A. The length of $\overline{NR}$ is 5 m.

B. The length of $\overline{PR}$ is 5 m.

C. The length of $\overline{GH}$ is 5 m.

D. The length of $\overline{GQ}$ is 5 m.

Geometry

Use triangle *ABC* for Questions 6 and 7.

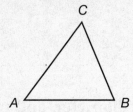

6. Make a congruent copy of triangle *ABC*.

7. Describe how you made your copy in Problem 7.

    _____

    _____

 Fill in the blanks.

8. The symbol that means "is congruent to" is _____.

9. If two polygons are congruent, their _____ sides are congruent.

10. Congruent figures have the same _____ and the same _____.

Circumference, Diameter, and Pi

Review It! When you work with circumference, diameter, and pi, remember these words:

circumference the distance around a circle

diameter a line segment with endpoints on a circle that passes through the center of the circle

ratio a comparison of two numbers

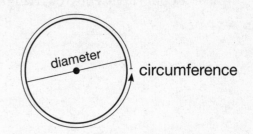

Find the circumference of the circle.

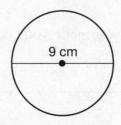

9 cm

Step 1 Write the ratio of circumference to the length of the diameter.

In **every circle,** the ratio of circumference (C) to the length of the diameter (d) is the same. That ratio is about 3.14, and is called pi. The Greek letter π stands for pi.

$$\frac{C}{d} = \pi$$

Step 2 Substitute for d and π.

$$\frac{C}{\square} = 3.14$$

> **THINK** π is pronounced the same as "pie."

Step 3 Multiply to find C.

$$\frac{C}{9} \times 9 = 3.14 \times 9$$

$$C = 28.26$$

So, the circumference of the circle is about _____.

Try It!   Find the circumference of each circle.

Ask Yourself

1.

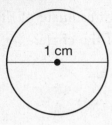

1 cm

_____

2.

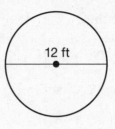

12 ft

_____

1.

What unit should you use for C? cm or cm²?

3.

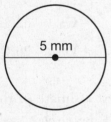

5 mm

_____

4.

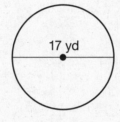

17 yd

_____

5.

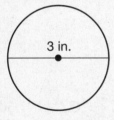

3 in.

_____

6.

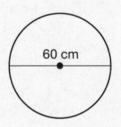

60 cm

_____

Solve.

7.   The U.S. Mint is making a different quarter to honor each of the 50 states. A quarter for Georgia was put out in 1999. The quarter has a diameter of about 24 mm. What is the circumference of the quarter? _____

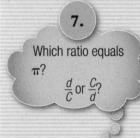

7.

Which ratio equals π?

$\frac{d}{C}$ or $\frac{C}{d}$?

8.   A circular swimming pool is 4 feet high and has a diameter of 20 feet. What is the circumference of the pool? _____

Geometry

1. Which is the best estimate of the circumference of the circle?

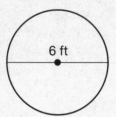

6 ft

A. 9.14 ft²

B. 9.14 ft

C. 18.84 ft²

D. 18.84 ft

2. Which is the best estimate of the circumference of the circle?

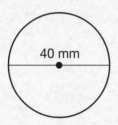

40 mm

A. 12.56 mm

B. 43.14 mm

C. 125.6 mm

D. 431.4 mm

3. The diameter of a dime is about 0.7 inches. Which is the best estimate of the circumference of a dime?

A. 1.4 in.   **C.** 2.8 in.

B. 2.2 in.   **D.** 3.8 in.

4. Which is the best estimate of the circumference of the circle?

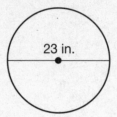

23 in.

A. 72.22 in.   **C.** 62.22 in.

B. 71.22 in.   **D.** 26.14 in.

5. Which is the best estimate of the circumference of the circle?

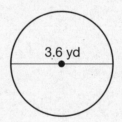

3.6 yd

A. 1.1304 yd   **C.** 11.304 yd

B. 6.74 yd   **D.** 113.04 yd

6. A coffee can is shaped like a cylinder 13 cm high. Its base is a circle with diameter of 10 cm. Which is the best estimate of the circumference of the base of this coffee can?

A. 13.14 cm

B. 16.14 cm

C. 31.4 cm

D. 40.82 cm

Geometry

A student measured the circumference and diameter of a circular pond. His measurements were $C = 350$ ft and $d = 70$ ft. Use this information for Questions 7 and 8.

7.   Use what you learned in this lesson to show that this student made a mistake in measuring.

_____

_____

8.   Suppose the student measured the diameter correctly. Find the circumference of the pond.

_____

 Fill in the blanks.

9.   The distance around a circle is called its _____ .

10.   The Greek letter _____ is used to represent a special ratio in circles.

11.   A ratio is a way to compare two numbers using _____ .

12.   A diameter is a _____ _____ whose endpoints are on a circle.

13.   A circle's diameter must pass through the _____ of that circle.

Representing Unknown Quantities

Review It!

When you are representing unknown quantities, remember these words:

variable a symbol or letter used to stand for a number

algebraic expression numbers and variables connected by operation signs $(+, -, \times, \div)$

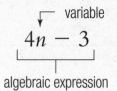

variable

$$4n - 3$$

algebraic expression

Tim is five years older than Kim. Will is one year younger than Kim. Jasper is five times as old as Kim. Write algebraic expressions to represent Kim's, Tim's, Will's, and Jasper's ages.

Step 1 Choose a variable to represent Kim's age.

Since Kim begins with K, let k represent Kim's age.

Step 2 Write an expression to represent Tim's age.

Tim is _____ years older than Kim. ◄┄┄┄┄┄ **THINK** "Older than" means *more than*.

So, $k + 5$ represents Tim's age.

Step 3 Write an expression to represent Will's age.

Will is one year younger than Kim. ◄┄┄┄┄┄ **THINK** "Younger than" means *less than*.

So, $k \bigcirc 1$ represents Will's age.

Step 4 Write an expression to represent Jasper's age.

Jasper is five times as old as Kim.

So, $5k$ represents Jasper's age. ◄┄┄┄┄┄ **THINK** $5k$ means $5 \times k$.

So, Kim's age is _____, Tim's age is _____, Will's age is _____, and Jasper's age is _____.

Algebra

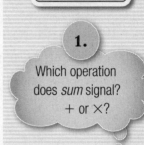

 Toni is thinking of a number. Let *n* stand for that number. Write an expression to represent each new number.

1. the sum of Toni's number and 8 _____

2. Toni's number divided by 17 _____

3. twice Toni's number _____

4. three more than Toni's number _____

5. twelve less than Toni's number _____

6. twelve reduced by Toni's number _____

7. the product of 9 and Toni's number _____

8. one-half of Toni's number _____

9. Toni's number increased by 118 _____

10. Toni's number decreased by 13 _____

1.

Which operation does *sum* signal?
+ or ✕?

Solve.

11. Joaquin and Alma work at a store. Joaquin works 12 hours less each week than Alma. Let *h* stand for the number of hours Alma works each week. Write an expression for the number of hours Joaquin works. _____

11.

Which operation does *less* tell you to use?
+ or −?

12. Georgia is about six times as large as Vermont. Let *v* stand for the number of square miles in Vermont. Write an expression for the number of square miles in Georgia.

_____

13. Robby's shirt cost *s* dollars. He paid the clerk using a $50 bill. Write an expression for the number of dollars Robby received in change. _____

Algebra

Circle the best answer for each question.

1. If x stands for a number Caroline is thinking of, which expression represents one-third of that number?

    A. $x \div 3$

    B. $3x$

    C. $x - 3$

    D. $x + 3$

2. Lee is nine years older than her brother Sandy. Let s stand for Sandy's age. Which expression represents Lee's age?

    A. $9s$

    B. $s \div 9$

    C. $s - 9$

    D. $s + 9$

3. The temperature was t degrees at noon yesterday. By 3:00 P.M., the temperature had fallen four degrees. Which expression represents the temperature at 3:00 P.M.?

    A. $3 - t$

    B. $4 - t$

    C. $t - 3$

    D. $t - 4$

4. There are 12 bagels in a dozen. Let d represent the number of dozens of bagels that Noel bought. Which expression represents the number of bagels Noel bought?

    A. $12 + d$

    B. $12d$

    C. $12 \div d$

    D. $d \div 12$

5. There are 120 students in the 5th grade. Let g stand for the number of girls in the fifth grade. Which expression represents the number of boys in the fifth grade?

    A. $120 - g$

    B. $120 + g$

    C. $g - 120$

    D. $120 \div g$

6. Carlo earns \$15 per hour. Let h stand for the number of hours he worked last week. Which expression represents the total amount Carlo earned last week?

    A. $15 + h$

    B. $15 \div h$

    C. $15h$

    D. $h \div 15$

Let *a* represent the attendance at Saturday's baseball game. The attendance was 300 less at Friday's game and 450 more at Sunday's game. Use this information for Questions 7 and 8.

7. Use *a* to write expressions to represent the attendance at Fridays' game and at Sunday's game.

    _____

8. Let *f* stand for the attendance at Friday's game. Use *f* to write expressions to represent the attendance at Saturday's game and at Sunday's game.

    _____

 Fill in the blanks.

9. In algebra, a symbol used to stand for a number is a _____.

10. The mathematical phrase $3 + x$ is an example of an _____ _____.

11. In the mathematical phrase $2n - 12$, the variable is _____.

Algebra

Evaluating Algebraic Expressions

 **Review It!** When you evaluate algebraic expressions, remember this word:

formula an equation that shows a relationship among different amounts

$D = RT$ is a common formula.

Distance   Rate   Time

Find the value of $13 + 7n$ when $n = 12$.

Step 1 Substitute for the variable.

$13 + 7n = 13 + 7 \times$ _____

> **REMEMBER** $7n$ means $7 \times n$.

Step 2 Evaluate the expression.

$13 + 7 \times 12 = 13 + 84$

$= $ _____

> **REMEMBER** $\times$ comes before $+$ in the order of operations.

So, when $n = 12$, $13 + 7n = $ _____.

Solve.

1. What is the value of $5m$ if $m = 8$? _____

2. What is the value of $2 + y$ if $y = 19$? _____

3. If $h = 14$, what is the value of $h \div 2$? _____

4. If $k = 10$, what is the value of $3k + 1$? _____

5. What is the value of $100 - x$ if $x = 42$? _____

6. What is the value of $8d \div 4$ if $d = 12$? _____

The formula $C = G - 3$ relates the time in Georgia (G) to the time in California (C). Use the formula for Questions 7–9.

7. If the time in Georgia is 8 P.M., what is the time in California? _____

8. If the time in Georgia is 11 A.M., what is the time in California? _____

9. If the time in California is 4 P.M., what is the time in Georgia? _____

Solve.

10. A plumber charges $30 for each job plus $40 for each hour worked. You can use the formula $c = 40h + 30$ to find the total amount in dollars, c, that the plumber charges. In this formula, h stands for the number of hours worked. What would the plumber charge for a 3-hour job? _____

11. If n people go to the amusement park, the total cost is $28n$ dollars. How much does it cost a group of 12 people to go to this amusement park? _____

Algebra

Circle the best answer for each question.

1. What is the value of 6*n* if *n* = 3?

A. 2

B. 9

C. 18

D. 63

2. What is the value of 42 − *h* if *h* = 28?

A. 14

B. 24

C. 60

D. 70

3. Zelda is paid $200 per week plus $50 for each new account she signs up. The total amount she earns in a week, *E*, can be found by using the formula *E* = 50*a* + 200, where *a* stands for the number of new accounts Zelda signs up. How much would Zelda earn in a week if she signed up 12 new accounts?

A. $10,936

B. $800

C. $700

D. $600

4. If *a* = 7 and *b* = 1, what is the value of 2*a* + *b*?

A. 9

B. 15

C. 16

D. 28

5. If *w* = 20, what is the value of 5*w* ÷ 10?

A. 10

B. 15

C. 25

D. 40

6. The formula *D* = *RT* can be used to find distance traveled (*D*) when you know the rate (*R*) and the amount of time (*T*). If Keith rides his bike at an average rate of 15 miles per hour for 3 hours, what distance will he travel?

A. 5 miles

B. 18 miles

C. 35 miles

D. 45 miles

Algebra

The formula $f = 3y$ converts yards (y) to feet (f). Use this formula for Questions 7 and 8.

7. Find the number of feet in 120 yards.

_____

8. Write a formula that could be used to convert feet to yards.

_____

 Math Words **Fill in the blanks.**

9. To find the value of $6x$ when $x = 10$, you _____ 10 for x.

10. In the expression $m - 11$, m is the _____.

11. In the expression $2g$, the operation is _____.

12. An equation that shows a mathematical relationship between different quantities is a _____.

Algebra

Analyzing Data from Graphs

Review It! When you analyze data from graphs, remember these words:

data numerical information

graph a way to show data

bar graph a graph that uses bars to show data

line graph a graph that uses points connected by line segments to show data

pictograph a graph that uses pictures to show data

Find how much the temperature increase from 10 A.M. to 12 P.M.

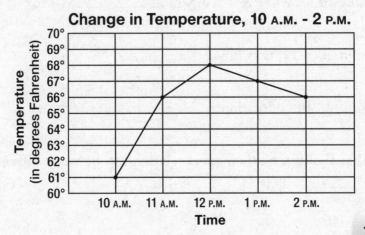

Change in Temperature, 10 A.M. - 2 P.M.

Step 1 Read the 10 A.M. temperature on the line graph: 61°F ◄···

Step 2 Read the 12 P.M. temperature on the line graph: 68°F

Step 3 Subtract to find the temperature change.

68 − _____ = _____

THINK Find 10 A.M. on the horizontal axis and then read up to the point on the graph.

So, the temperature increased by _____°F.

Try It! Use the pictograph for Questions 1–3.

Rainy Days in Kell Valley

2006	🌢🌢🌢🌢
2005	🌢🌢🌢
2004	🌢🌢🌢🌢🌢🌢
2003	🌢🌢🌢🌢🌢

Key: 🌢 = 10 days

1. How many rainy days were there in 2004? _____

2. Which year had the fewest rainy days? _____

3. How many more rainy days were there in 2004 than in 2006? _____

1.

How many rainy days does one symbol represent? 1, 2, 5, or 10?

Use the bar graph for Questions 4–6.

Students' Favorite Seasons

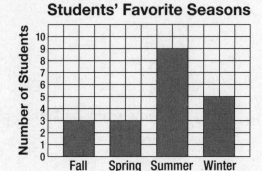

4. How many more students chose Summer than Spring? _____

5. Which two seasons were chosen by the same number of students? _____

6. How many students were surveyed in all? _____

4.

How many students chose Summer? 3, 5, or 9?

Data Analysis

123

On Your Own!

Circle the best answer for each question.

Use the line graph for Questions 1 and 2.

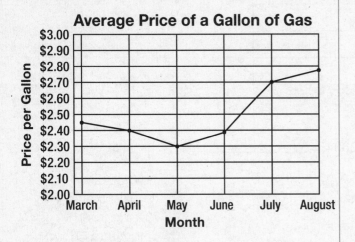

Use the bar graph for Questions 3 and 4.

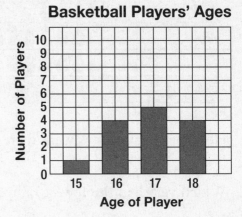

1. In which month was the average price of a gallon of gas lowest?

    A. March

    B. April

    C. May

    D. August

2. Between which two months did the average price increase the most?

    A. April and May

    B. May and June

    C. June and July

    D. July and August

3. What is the most common age of the basketball players?

    A. 18

    B. 17

    C. 16

    D. 15

4. How many basketball players are there in all?

    A. 14

    B. 13

    C. 12

    D. 11

Use the line graph shown on Page 124.

5. Explain how the average price of a gallon of gas changed during the six months.

_____

_____

_____

6. How can you tell when the average price is greatest?

_____

 Fill in the blanks.

7. Data is numerical _____.

8. A graph that uses pictures to show data is called a_____.

9. A graph that uses points connected by line segments to show data is called a

_____ _____.

Data Analysis

Comparing and Contrasting Graphic Representations

 **Review It!**

When you compare and contrast graphic representations, remember this word:

circle graph a graph that uses a circle divided into sections to show data

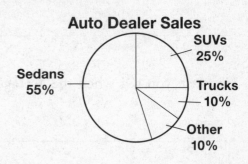

Auto Dealer Sales
Sedans 55%
SUVs 25%
Trucks 10%
Other 10%

Describe how line graphs and circle graphs are used _differently_ to represent data.

Step 1 Think about line graphs.

Line graphs use points connected by _____ _____ to show data.

Line graphs are good for showing numbers at different points in time.

Line graphs allow you to see change over time, and see trends.

You could use a line graph to show the population of a town over 20 years.

Step 2 Think about circle graphs.

Circle graphs divide one whole circle into parts, or categories.

Circle graphs make it easy to compare the sizes of different categories.

Circle graphs make it easy to compare a part to a whole.

You could use a circle graph to show a family's budget.

Try It! **Which type of graph would you use to show the data? Write** *bar graph, circle graph, line graph,* **or** *pictograph.* **Explain your choice.**

Ask Yourself

1. Todd wants to show how the price of a stock he owns has increased over the past five years.

_____

_____

1.

Which graph best shows change over time?
Bar, circle, or line?

2. Ami, Brie, Celia, and Dee are pitchers on a softball team. The coach wants to make a graph that shows each pitcher's wins for the season.

_____

_____

3. Mr. Li runs a company that recycles metal. He wants to make a graph that shows how the company's $1 million budget is spent each year.

_____

_____

3.

Which graph lets you compare parts to the whole?
Bar, circle, or line?

4. Flavia called four babysitters to find out how much each one charged per hour. The amounts were very different.

_____

_____

Data Analysis

Circle the best answer for each question.

1. Which would be the best time to use a circle graph?

   A. To show the increase in the cost of oil over 10 years

   B. To show the different prices four stores charge for a pair of sneakers

   C. To show how many miles a family drove each day on a vacation

   D. To show the number of votes that four candidates received in an election

2. As part of a science experiment, Christie is keeping track of a liquid's temperature as it cools. She is recording the temperature each minute in a table. Christie wants to show her data in a graph. Which type of graph would be best to show Christie's data?

   A. bar graph

   B. circle graph

   C. line graph

   D. pictograph

3. Deacon Motors sold 8 sedans, 12 SUVs, and 5 convertibles last month. Which type of graph should NOT be used to show this data?

   A. bar graph

   B. circle graph

   C. line graph

   D. pictograph

4. In the past five years, the number of cell phones sold at a store has increased from 100 to 1,000. The store owner wants to make a graph that shows how sales have increased each year. Which type of graph is LEAST likely to do this well?

   A. bar graph

   B. circle graph

   C. line graph

   D. pictograph

Use the bar graph for Questions 5 and 6.

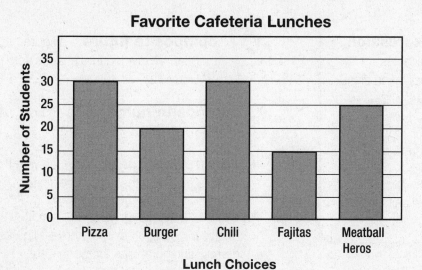

Favorite Cafeteria Lunches

5. What other kind of graph could you use to show this data?

_____

6. What kind of graph would NOT be a good choice for showing this data?

_____

Math Words

Draw a line to match each type of graph to its description.

7. bar graph — used like a bar graph

8. circle graph — allows you to easily compare categories

9. line graph — allows you to compare parts to the whole

10. pictograph — allows you to spot trends over time

Data Analysis

Math Words

A

algebraic expression numbers and variables connected by operation signs $(+, -, \times, \div)$ (Lesson 28)

altitude a line segment used to measure height in a parallelogram or triangle (Lesson 19)

area the number of square units inside a figure (Lesson 18)

B

bar graph a graph that uses bars to show data (Lesson 30)

C

capacity the amount a container can hold (Lesson 23)

center the point inside a circle that is the same distance from all points on the circle (Lesson 21)

circle a closed figure with all points on the circle the same distance from its center (Lesson 21)

circle graph a graph (or pie chart) used to show parts of a whole (Lesson 17); a graph that uses a circle divided into sections to show data (Lesson 31)

circumference the distance around a circle (Lesson 27)

common denominator a denominator that two or more fractions have (Lesson 12)

C

composite figure a figure that can be divided into shapes you know (Lesson 22)

composite number a number with more than two factors (Lesson 2)

congruent figures figures with the same shape and the same size (Lesson 26)

corresponding angles matching angles in two figures; in congruent figures, corresponding angles are congruent. (Lesson 26)

corresponding sides matching sides in two figures; in congruent figures, corresponding sides are congruent. (Lesson 26)

D

data numerical information (Lesson 30)

decimal a number with whole number places and places less than 1 (Lesson 4)

decimal point a period used to separate the whole number places from the places less than 1 in a decimal (Lesson 4)

denominator the number in a fraction below the bar (Lesson 8)

diameter a line segment with endpoints on a circle that passes through the center of the circle (Lesson 27)

dividend a number being divided (Lesson 5)

D

divisibility rule a way to test if one number is divisible by another number (Lesson 3)

divisible a number is divisible by a second number if the second number divides evenly into the first number (Lesson 3)

divisor the number you are dividing by (Lesson 5)

 E

equivalent fractions fractions that have the same value (Lesson 8)

 F

factor when two whole numbers are multiplied, each is a factor of the product (Lesson 1)

formula an equation that shows a relationship among different amounts (Lesson 29)

fraction a number used to name part of a whole or part of a group (Lesson 8)

 G

graph a way to show data (Lesson 30)

greatest common factor (GCF) the largest number that is a factor of two or more numbers (Lesson 11)

 I

improper fraction a fraction whose numerator is greater than or equal to its denominator (Lesson 9)

 $\cong$ is congruent to

 L

least common denominator (LCD) the smallest denominator that two or more fractions have (the LCM of the denominators) (Lesson 12)

least common multiple (LCM) the smallest number that is a multiple of two or more numbers (Lesson 11)

line graph a graph that uses points connected by line segments to show data (Lesson 30)

lowest terms a phrase used to describe a fraction that can't be simplified any more (Lesson 8)

M

mixed number a number with a whole number part and a fraction part (Lesson 9)

multiple the product of a whole number and a counting number (1, 2, 3, 4, ...) (Lesson 1)

 N

numerator the number in a fraction above the bar (Lesson 8)

parallelogram a quadrilateral with two pairs of parallel sides (Lesson 19)

percent a ratio of a number to 100 (Lesson 17)

pictograph a graph that uses pictures to show data (Lesson 30)

polygon a closed figure with straight sides (Lesson 18)

prime number a number with exactly two factors, 1 and itself (Lesson 2)

product the result of multiplication (Lesson 1)

quotient the result of division (Lesson 5)

radius a line segment from the center of a circle to any point on the circle (Lesson 21)

ratio a comparison of two numbers (Lesson 27)

reciprocal for any fraction, its reciprocal is found by exchanging its numerator and denominator (Lesson 10)

rectangular prism a solid figure with all faces shaped like rectangles (Lesson 24)

round to use a simpler estimate of a number (Lesson 16)

variable a symbol or letter used to stand for a number (Lesson 28)

volume a measure of the space enclosed by a three-dimensional figure (Lesson 24)

My Math Words